PRIMARY MATHEMATICS 4B Home Instructor's Guide

Authored by: Jennifer Hoerst
Printed by: Avyx, Inc.

Published by Avyx, Inc.
Reprinted 2005, 2007, 2010

Go to:
www.avyx.com

Or e-mail:
info@avyx.dom

Or write:
Avyx, Inc.
8032 South Grant Way
Littleton, CO 80122-2705
USA
303-483-0140

ISBN 13: 978-1-887-84080-4

Printed in the United States of America

Preface and General Instructions

This guide is meant to help instructors using *Primary Mathematics 3B* when teaching one student or a small group of students. It should be used as a guide and adapted as needed. It contains

 objectives,

 notes to the instructor, providing added explanation of concepts,

 instructional ideas and suggested activities,

 and ideas for games

to reinforce concepts from the

 corresponding textbook pages, learning tasks, and

 "homework" assignments.

Included is a suggested weekly schedule and pages for mental math (in the appendix). The schedule is simply to help you keep on track – you need to spend more time on a topic if necessary and less time if your student is proficient in the topic. Practices and reviews in the text are scheduled as they are encountered, and can be done independently by the student, or can be used as part of a lesson. Since some of the practice questions are challenging, they provide good opportunities for discussion. When there are several practices one after the other, you may want to go on to the next topic and insert the rest of the practices later to allow for more ongoing review. The mental math pages can be used as worksheets and many can also be done orally, with your student seeing the problem and answering out loud rather than writing the answer down. They can be used any time after they are referenced in this guide, and can be used more than once for more practice. So if four Mental Math pages are listed for one lesson, they are not meant to all be done during that lesson, but can be used any time after that lesson for review and mental math practice.

Answers to the workbook exercises are given at the end of this guide.

This guide can be used with both the third edition and the U.S. edition of *Primary Mathematics 4B*.

3d› indicates portions pertaining only to the third edition, and

US› indicates portions pertaining only to the US edition (except for number words).

U.S. spellings and conventions will be used in this guide. Answers involving number words will use the current U.S. convention of reserving the word "and" for the decimal and not using it in number words for whole numbers.

Contents

Answers to Workbook Exercises and Reviews

Appendix

Weekly Schedule

	Part	Lesson	Text Pages	Workbook Exercises	Mental Math (appendix)	Material
Unit 1 : Decimals						
1	1 Tenths	(1) Tenths	6-8	1		Base-10 blocks Fraction squares Number lines Number discs Place-value chart
		(2) Ones and Tenths	9-10	2		
		(3) Tenths and Mixed Fractions	10	3		
		(4) Numbers to One Decimal Place	11	4		
	2 Hundredths	(1) Hundredths I	12-15	5		
2		(2) Hundredths II	15-16	6		Coins and dollar bills Fraction squares Number discs Place-value chart Number cube
		(3) Hundredths III	16-17	7		
		(4) Decimal numbers and Fractions	17	8	1	
		(5) Comparing Hundredths	18-19	9		
		(6) Add or Subtract Tenths or Hundredths	19	10	2-3	
3	3 Thousandths	(1) Thousandths	20-21	11		Base-10 blocks Number discs Place-value chart Number cube
		(2) Comparing Thousandths	21	12	4	
		(3) Thousandths and Fractions	22	13		
		(4) Practice	23-24			
4	4 Rounding Off	(1) Round to a Whole Number	25-27	14		Number lines
		(2) Round to One Decimal Place	27	15		
Review						
4 5	Review		28-30	Review 1-3		
Unit 2 : The Four Operations of Decimals						
6	1 Addition and Subtraction	(1) Adding 1-Place Decimals	31- 33	16-17	5	Number discs Base-10 blocks Place-value chart Number cube Counters Index cards
		(2) Adding 2-Place Decimals	34-35	18-19	6	
		(3) Subtracting Tenths	36	20	7	
		(4) Subtracting Hundredths	37-38	21	8, 9	
7		(5) Subtracting 1-Place Decimals	38	22	10	Number discs Base-10 blocks Place-value chart Number cube Playing cards
		(6) Subtracting 2-Place Decimals	39	23-24		
		(7) Estimation, Other Mental Strategies	40	25	11	
		(8) Word Problems	41-42	26-27		
8		(9) Practice	43-44			

	Part	Lesson	Text Pages	Workbook Exercises	Mental Math (appendix)	Material
	2 Multiplication	(1) Multiplication of Tenths and Hundredths	45-47	28	12	Number discs Base-10 blocks Place-value chart Money
		(2) Multiplication of Decimals I		29	13	
9		(3) Multiplication of Decimals II	48-49	30-31		Number discs Base-10 blocks Place-value chart Money
		(4) Word Problems	50-51	32-33		
		(5) Practice	52-53			
	3 Division	(1) Division of Decimals I	53-55	34	14	
10		(2) Division of Decimals II	56	35		Number discs Base-10 blocks Place-value chart Money
		(3) Division of Decimals III	56-57	36		
		(4) Division of Decimals IV	58	37		
		(5) Estimation and Rounding	59	38		
		(6) Word Problems	60-61	39-40		
11		(7) Practice	62-64		15	
Review						
	Review		65-67			
Unit 3 : Measures						
12	1 Multiplication	(1) Multiplication of Compound Units	68-69			Appendix Ex. 3.1
		(2) Division of Compound Units	70-71	41		
		(3) Practice	72-73			
Review						
	Review			Review 4-5		
Unit 4 : Symmetry						
13	1 Symmetric Figures	(1) Symmetric Figures	74-75	42		Mirror
		(2) Lines of Symmetry	76-79	43		
		(3) Complete Symmetric Figures	79	44		
14		Review	80-85			
Unit 5 : Solid Figures						
15	1 Identifying Solid Figures	(1) Building Solids from Cubes I	86-87	45		Multilink cubes 1-cm unit cubes 1-cm graph paper Isometric dot paper Meter stick Rulers
		(2) Building Solids from Cubes 2	88-89	46		
		(3) Making New Solids	89	47		
Unit 6 : Volume						
16	1 Cubic Units	(1) Cubic Units	90-92	48-49		Multilink cubes 1-cm cubes Base-10 blocks Centimeter graph paper
	2 Volume of a Cuboid	(1) Volume	93-96	50		
		(2) Liter	97	51		
		(3) Practice	98-99			
Review						1 week
17	Review		100-104	Review 6-7		

Additional Material

Base-10 set.

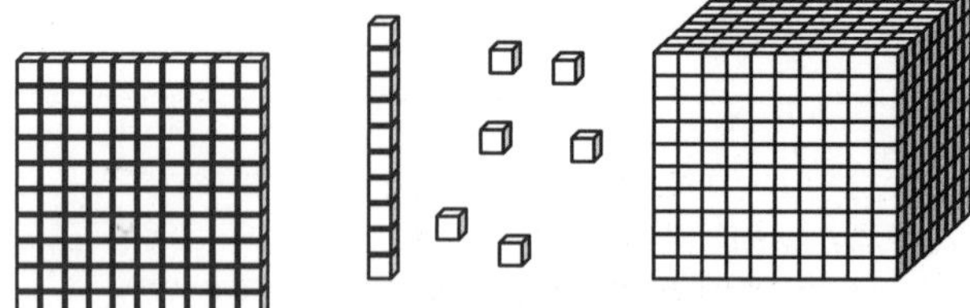

Number discs - Use plastic or cardboard discs and write "100" on ten discs, "10" on twenty discs, "1" on twenty discs, "0.1" on twenty discs, "0.01" on twenty discs, and "0.001" on twenty discs.

Multilink cubes that can connect to form a 3-dimensional object.

Place-Value Chart
Make one large enough to hold up to nine number discs each in the top and bottom halves. Or just draw one on a whiteboard laid flat or paper as needed.

Tens	Ones	Tenths	Hundredths	Thousandths

Fraction squares
Squares showing whole, tenths, and hundredths. You can copy the ones in the appendix.

Index cards for number cards and fact cards.

Playing cards or **4 sets of number cards 0-10**
Use two decks. For one deck, remove the face cards and white out the 1 and the symbols on the tens card to make it into a 0. Aces are ones. For the other deck, remove the face cards but leave the tens.

Number cubes – Use blank cubes and labels, or cover regular dice with masking tape squares.

12-inch ruler - Should show inches on one side and centimeters on the other. Use one that shows 16ths from 0 to 6 inches and tenths from 6 to 12 inches, if possible.

Mirror – A small mirror with at least one straight edge.

Math Mirror (optional) – These are commercially available and have a transparent red surface which both reflects the figure on one side and allows you to see through to the paper on the other side.

Unit 1 – Decimal numbers

Part 1 – Tenths

(1) Tenths (pp. 6-8)

- Read and write 1-place decimal numbers less than 1.
- Express a fraction with a denominator of 10 as a decimal number.
- Express a 1-place decimal number as a fraction with a denominator of 10.
- Read a scale in tenths.
- Make a whole with 1-place decimal numbers.

In *Primary Mathematic 2B*, students were introduced to 2-place decimal numbers in the context of money. The dollar is the whole, there are 100 cents in a dollar, and cents are written after a dot. The dot was not called a decimal point at that level.

Use base-10 blocks to discuss place-value down to tenths. Draw four columns, labeling the top hundreds, tens, and ones. Save one column to add the label tenths.

Discussion:	Write:	Hun-dreds	Tens	Ones	Tenths
Get the thousand-cube. What is one-tenth of 1,000?	$\frac{1}{10}$ of 1,000 = 100	**1**	**0**	**0**	
Get a hundred-flat. What is one-tenth of 100?	$\frac{1}{10}$ of 100 = 10		**1**	**0**	
Get a ten-rod. What is one-tenth of 10?	$\frac{1}{10}$ of 10 = 1			**1**	
Get a unit-cube. Imagine the unit cube is expanded to be as big as the	$\frac{1}{10}$ of 1 = 0.1			**0** •	**1**

hundred-flat. Get the hundred-flat and think of it as equal to one whole. What is one-tenth of 1? Get a ten-rod and imagine it to be one-tenth of 1. We move one place value over for each tenth. So to write one-tenth, we make a new place value, called tenths. (Label the "tenths" column.) We separate the place values that are for less than a whole from those for whole numbers with a dot, called a **decimal point**. (Write a dot between the columns.). If the number has no whole part, we usually write a 0 in front of the decimal point.

Point out that each place in a number is one tenth of the place to the left, or ten times the place to the right.

Use **fraction squares** showing tenths (such the ones in the appendix), or use the 100-flat from a base-10 set, calling it a one, and lay 10-rods on top if it, or use the reverse side of a laminated hundred-chart and dry-erase markers. Color in some rows and have your student give the amount colored as both a fraction and a decimal number. For example, color in 3 rows. Your student writes $\frac{3}{10}$ and 0.3.

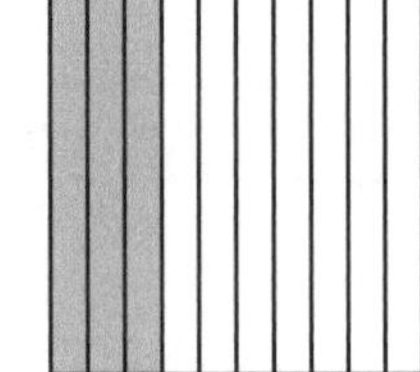

Write 1-place decimal numbers less than 1 and have your student color in the correct number of tenths.

Draw a number line. Show the 0 to 1 interval expanded and divide it into tenths. There is one in the appendix on page a18. Have your student label it as a fraction scale and as a decimal number scale. Note the relationship between decimal number numbers and fractions.

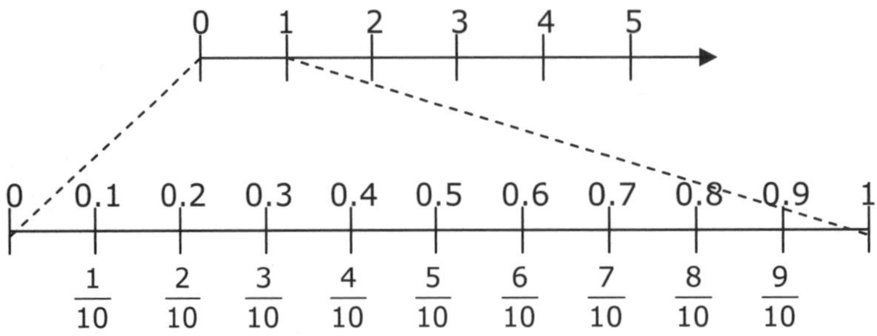

Write some 1-place decimal number numbers between 0 and 1. Tell your student that the number is one part of a whole and ask for the other part. Write the equation. For example:

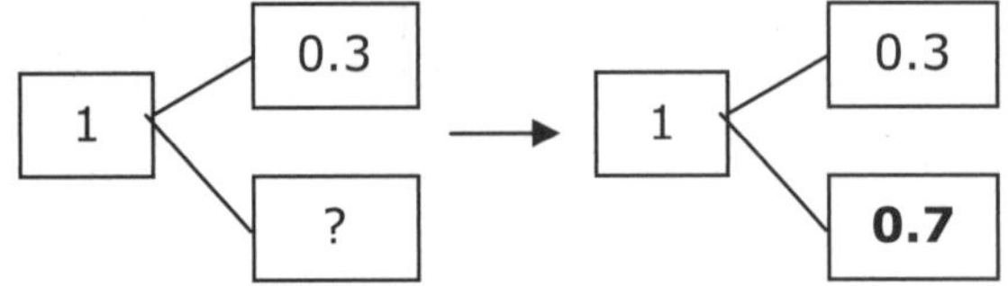

0.3 + 0.7 = 1

Page 6-7
Learning Tasks 1-4, pp. 7-8

1. (a) 0.4 (b) 0.6 (c) 0.9
2. (a) 0.1 (b) 0.3 (c) 0.5 (c) 0.7
3. 10
4. 4

Workbook Exercise 1

(2) Ones and Tenths (pp. 9-10)

- Read and write 1-place decimal numbers less 10 to one decimal place.
- Read scales in tenths.

In *Primary Mathematics*, decimal numbers are read as the whole number, "point," and then each digit in the decimal number. For example, 1.2 is read "one point two," 1.23 is read "one point two three," and 1.234 is read as "one point two three four." Some texts emphasize the relationship between decimal numbers and fractions by requiring the decimal number to be read as a fraction; thus 1.2 is read as "one and two tenths, " and 1.23 is read as "one and twenty-three hundredths," and 1.234 is read as "one and two hundred thirty-four thousandths." You may want to teach both ways of reading decimal numbers.

➤ Use **fraction squares** showing wholes and tenths, or use 100-flats and 10-rods from a base-10 set. Tell your student that the flat is one whole and so each rod is a tenth. Give your student some wholes and some tenths. Ask her to write the amount first as a fraction, and then as the corresponding decimal number. For example,

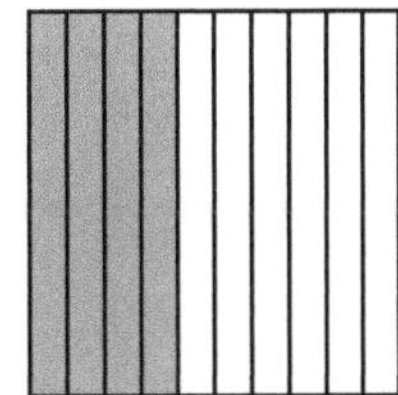

$2\frac{4}{10} = 2.4$

Tell her that this is read as "two point four" or "two and four tenths." It is four tenths more than 2.

Write some other mixed fractions greater than 1 with a denominator of 10 and ask your student to write them as a decimal number. Try some improper fractions. For example,

$$\frac{35}{10} = 3\frac{5}{10} = 3.5$$

➤ Use number lines such as those in the appendix on page a20 showing tenths. Ask your student to locate some 1-place decimal numbers such as 3.2, 6.4, 22.9. Point to a division and have her supply the decimal number for that point on the line.

Use a ruler. Show your student the divisions on the centimeter side. Each division is a tenth. Have him measure or draw some lengths correct to the nearest tenth and write the length as a 1-place decimal number.

On some rulers the inches from 6 inches to 12 inches are divided into tenths. Write a 1-place decimal number between 6 and 12 and have your student draw a line of the given length.

If you have some beakers or graduated cylinders, you can have her measure or read some volumes to the nearest tenth.

Learning Tasks 5-8, pp. 9-10

5. (a) 0.6 (b) 0.6
6. (a) 2.4 (b) 2.8
7. (a) 1.5 (b) 2.9
8. A 0.4 B 0.9 C 1.1 D 1.6

Workbook Exercise 2

(3) Tenths and Mixed Fractions (p. 10)

- Express a 1-place decimal number as a fraction in its simplest form.
- Compare and order numbers of up to one decimal place.

Remind your student that the simplest form of a fraction is the equivalent fraction where the denominator is as small as you can make it.

Ask her to write 0.5 as a fraction in its simplest form. $0.5 = \frac{5}{10} = \frac{1}{2}$

Learning Task 9, p. 10

9. (a) $\frac{1}{5}$ (b) $1\frac{1}{5}$ (c) $\frac{4}{5}$ (d) $2\frac{4}{5}$

Eventually, your student should be able to recall certain common decimal number/fraction equivalencies. If he remembers the decimal number for the unit fraction, he can find the others with the same denominator by multiplication:

$\frac{1}{5} = 0.2$; therefore $\frac{2}{5} = 0.4$ (2 x 0.2), $\frac{3}{5} = 0.6$, $\frac{4}{5} = 0.8$

Write the numbers 2 and 1.2.

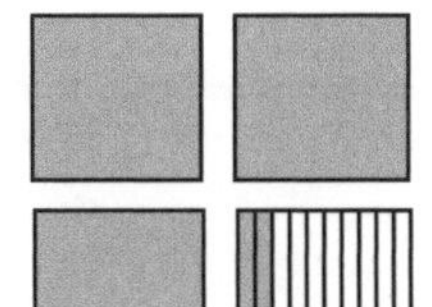

Ask your student which is larger. 2 is larger even though it has only one digit. Illustrate with **fraction squares** or with base-10 blocks where the 100-flat is one and the 10-rod is one tenth. Caution your student that with decimal numbers we need to pay attention to the place value of each digit when comparing the numbers, and not the number of digits. 12 is larger than 2, but 1.2 is smaller than 2 because there is only one whole rather than two. We can think of 2 as 2.0. Your student can write the numbers being compared vertically, aligning the decimals, and then compare each place, starting from the largest place value.

Learning Tasks 10-12, p. 10

10. 3.7

11. 8.5

12. (a) 0.3, 1.3, 3, 3.1
    (b) 2.7, 7.2, 7.8, 9

Workbook Exercise 3

(4) Numbers to One Decimal number Place (p. 11)

- Interpret 1-place decimal numbers in terms of tens, ones, and tenths.

Use two **fraction squares** showing tenths. Tape them together and color 14 tenths. Or use base-10 blocks, reminding your student that the flat is now a one and the rod a tenth and give him 14 rods. Ask him to write a decimal number for it. He should write 1.4. He may write 0.14, which is incorrect. Show him that he can trade in 10 tenths for 1 whole. There can be no more than 9 tenths in the tenth place value. If there are 10 tenths, they become a 1. So 14 tenths must be renamed as 1 one and 4 tenths.

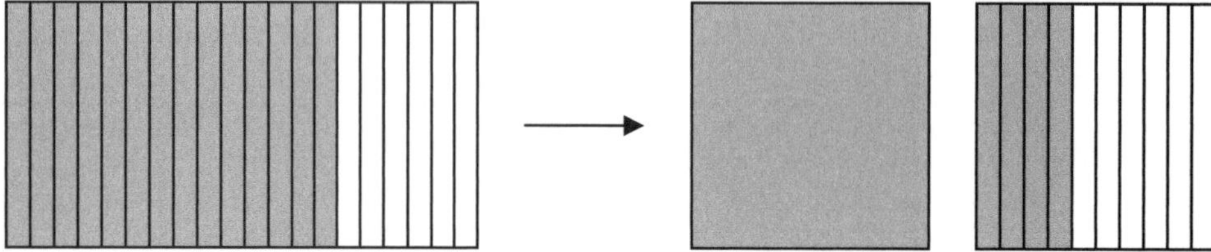

Ask:

- How many tenths are there in 0.4? (4)
- How many tenths are there in 1? (10)
- How many tenths are there in 1.4? (14)
- How many tenths are in 2? (20)
- What is the decimal number for 42 tenths? (4.2)

Use **number discs** labeled with 10, 1, and 0.1. Mix them up in a bowl or bag. Draw a place value chart with 3 columns labeled *tens*, *ones*, and *tenths*. Have your student pick up a handful of discs and arrange them on the place value chart. If he has more than 10 of any one kind of number disc, he must trade it in for the next higher place value. Then he writes the corresponding decimal number. Rewrite the decimal number in expanded form, for example:

42.8 = 40 + 2 + 0.8

Point out that the number is made up of two parts, the whole part 42, and the fractional, or part of a whole, part, 0.8. The decimal number point separates the whole part from the fractional part.

Repeat with other handfuls of discs as needed.

Write a number, such as 20.6, and ask your student for the number of tenths, ones, and tens.

Write some equations such as the following and have your student supply the decimal number. If necessary, use **number discs** to illustrate.

- $10 + 0.2 = ?$ 10.2
- $0.4 + 4 + 10 = ?$ 14.4
- $6 + 0.2 + 30 = ?$ 36.2
- $100 + \frac{3}{10} + 2 = ?$ 102.3
- $30 + ? + 4 = 34.2$ 0.2
- $200 + ? + 0.4 = 243.4$ 43

Learning Tasks 13-14, p. 11

13. (a) 2.3 (b) 36.5 (c) 50.4

14. (a) 1.2 (b) 2.1

Draw a number

Material: Number discs (10's, 1's, 0.1's) in a bag.

Procedure: Each person picks out 20 discs without looking at them first, and then writes the corresponding decimal number, renaming if necessary. The player with the highest number wins a point.

Workbook Exercise 4

Part 2 Hundredths

(1) Hundredths I (pp. 12-15)

- Read and write 2-place decimal numbers.
- Express a fraction less than one with a denominator of 10 or 100 as a decimal number.
- Relate 2-place decimal numbers to hundredths.
- Interpret 2-place decimal numbers in terms of hundreds, tens, ones, tenths, and hundredths.

Use **base-10 blocks** to discuss place-value down to hundredths. Show your student the flat and remind her that the flat now stands for one whole. The rod stands for one tenth. Ask her what the unit, or one square on the flat, would stand for. It is one hundredth, or $\frac{1}{100}$ of a whole. Remind her that when writing numbers, each place is one tenth of the place to the left. Show her the rod, which stands for one tenth, and point out one square on the rod. It is one tenth of the tenth. So one hundredth of one is one tenth of one tenth; or, there are ten hundredths in a tenth and ten tenths in one. Emphasize the "th" sound in hundred**th** and ten**th** when speaking.

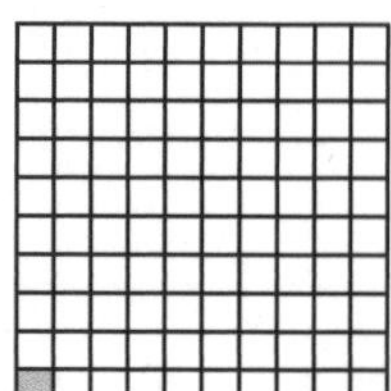

Ask her how she would write one hundredth as a decimal number. Hopefully, she will write 0.01. If not, write it for her, and point out that the 1 is in the hundredth place.

Give her 15 little cubes, and remind her that these are now hundredths. Ask her to write the decimal number for them. She should write 0.15. If she writes 0.015, remind her that no more than 9 can go in a place value, so 15 hundredths needs to be renamed as 1 tenth and 5 hundredths. Show her that ten cubes, or ten hundredths, make a ten, and trade them in for a tenth rod. If she needs more explanation, write four columns on some paper or a white-board laid flat, label the columns from left to right 10's, 1's, 0.1's and 0.01's. Hand her little cubes one at a time to put in the last column. When she gets the tenth cube, remind her that no more than 9 can go in a column. She needs to trade them in for a tenth, which is the same as ten hundredths.

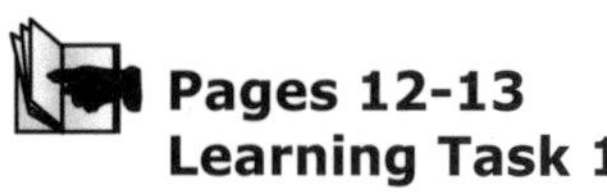

Pages 12-13
Learning Task 1

1. (a) 0.03 (b) 0.05 (c) 0.12

Use **number discs** (10's, 1's, 0.1's, and 0.01's) and a **place-value chart** with the columns tens, ones, tenths and hundredths. Mix up the number discs. Have your student pick up a handful of discs and arrange them on the place value chart. If she has more than 10 of any one kind of number disc, she must trade it in for the next higher place value. Then she writes the corresponding decimal number. Rewrite the decimal number in expanded form, for example:

$$42.84 = 40 + 2 + 0.8 + 0.04$$

Repeat as needed.

If she hasn't drawn some where one place value is missing, give her some discs of each kind, but leave out one kind. For example, give her three 10's, no 1's, six 0.1's, and four 0.01's and have her write the number.

$$30 + 0.6 + 0.04 = 30.64$$

Remind her that 0 is a place-holder. Here it shows that there are no ones.

Write a number, such as 20.62 and ask your student how many hundredths, tenths, ones, or tens there are.

Learning Tasks 2-4, p. 14

2. (a) 3.02 (b) 4.25
3. 3 stands for 30, 4 stands for 4, 5 stands for 0.5, 6 stands for 0.06
4. 0.9, 0.02

Draw a number

Material: Number discs (10's, 1's, 0.1's, 0.01's) in a bag.

Procedure: Each person picks out 10 discs without looking at them first, and then writes the corresponding decimal number. The player with the highest number wins a point.

Workbook Exercise 5

(2) Hundredths II (p. 15-16)

- Express a mixed number with a denominator of 100 as a decimal number.
- Relate cents to decimal numbers.

Students have already learned to express money as decimal numbers in earlier levels of *Primary Mathematics*, though the term decimal number was not used. In *Primary Mathematics 4A*, the student learned to express a part as a fraction of a whole. Both concepts are reviewed in this section.

Learning Task 5, p. 15

5. (a) 0.4 (b) 1.28 (c) 2.05

Do other examples as needed, using **fraction squares**. Color in a part, and have your student supply the fraction and decimal number. Or, give your student a fraction or a decimal number, and have him color in the correct number of squares.

Use some **coins and dollar bills**. Tell your student that a dollar bill is one whole. Give him a penny and ask him to write the penny as a fraction of a dollar and as a decimal number. He should write $\frac{1}{100}$ and \$0.01. Do the same with a dime. He should write $\frac{1}{10}$ and \$0.10. Point out that with money, we include the number of hundredths even if there aren't any. We write \$0.10 instead of \$0.1. \$1.40 is read as "a dollar and forty cents," not as "a dollar point four" or "a dollar and four tenths." Give him a dollar and 4 cents and ask him to write it as a decimal number. (\$1.04) Point out that the 0 is a place holder here too, showing that it is less than ten cents. The 4 cents is $\frac{4}{100}$ of one dollar, so we can't write \$1.4, since that would mean $1\frac{4}{10}$ dollars, or one dollar and forty cents.

Learning Tasks 6-7, p. 16

6. (a) 1 (b) 1
   (c) 2 (d) 5
   (e) 45 (f) 26

7. (a) \$3.85 (b) \$6.50
   (c) \$8.05 (d) \$85

Workbook Exercise 6

(3) Hundredths III (pp. 16-17)

- Interpret 2-place decimal numbers in terms of hundreds, tens, ones, tenths, and hundredths.
- Evaluate number patterns involving decimal numbers.
- Read scales in hundredths.

Learning Tasks 8-9, pp. 16-17

8. (a) 2.84 (b) 36.25
   (c) 54.03 (d) 80.57

9. (a) A 0.04 B 0.07 C 0.11 D 0.13 E 0.19
   (b) P 4.62 Q 4.66 R 4.69 S 4.73 T 4.78

For additional practice, write some equations such as the following and have your student supply the decimal number. If necessary, illustrate with **number discs**.

❖ $10 + 0.2 + 0.04 = ?$	10.24
❖ $0.44 + 4 + 40 = ?$	44.44
❖ $6 + 0.2 + 30 + \frac{1}{100} = ?$	36.21
❖ $100 + \frac{3}{10} + 0.02 + 8 = ?$	108.32
❖ $30 + ? + 4 = 34.02$	0.02
❖ $300 + ? + 0.05 = 136.05$	36
❖ 450 tenths = ?	45
❖ 450 hundredths = ?	4.5
❖ 4 tens, 62 tenths, 8 hundredths = ?	46.28
❖ 3.33 = ? hundredths	333
❖ $\frac{34}{100} + 100 = ?$	100.34
❖ $4 + \frac{1}{5} + \frac{6}{100} = ?$	4.26

➤ Discuss the following patterns with your student and have her supply the next two numbers.

❖ 1.7, 1.8, 1.9, ____ , ____	2, 2.1
❖ 0.4, 0.6, 0.8, ____, ____	1, 1.2
❖ 0.5, 1, 1.5, 2, 2.5, ____, ____	3, 3.5
❖ 0.07, 0.08, 0.09, ____, ____	0.1, 0.11
❖ 0.05, 0.1, 0.15, 0.2, ____, ____	0.25, 0.3
❖ 0.25, 0.5, 0.75, ____, ____	1, 1.25

 **Workbook Exercise 7**

(4) Decimals and Fractions (p. 17)

- Express a 2-place decimal number as a fraction in its simplest form.
- Express a fraction with a denominator that is a factor of 100 as a decimal number.

Ask your student to write 1.24 as a fraction. She may write

$$1.24 = 1\frac{24}{100}$$

Discuss how this can be simplified. It can be done in steps:

$$1.24 = 1\frac{24}{100} = 1\frac{12}{50} = 1\frac{6}{25}$$

Now ask her to write 0.25 as a fraction in its simplest form.

$$0.25 = \frac{25}{100} = \frac{1}{4}$$

Point out that in some cases we can think in terms of quarters. $0.25 is one quarter of a dollar, or one fourth of a dollar. So it is $\frac{1}{4}$. Your student should memorize certain common decimal number/fraction equivalencies.

$$0.25 = \frac{1}{4} \qquad 0.75 = \frac{3}{4} \qquad 0.20 = \frac{1}{5} \quad 0.50 = \frac{1}{2}$$

Since the factors of 100 are 2, 4, 5, 10, 20, 25, and 50, all decimal numbers to two place value rewritten as fractions in their simplest form will have one of these in the denominator. A quick way of finding the equivalent fraction is to divide the numerator by 5 or 2 successively. If it cannot be divided by 5 or 2, it cannot be simplified any further.

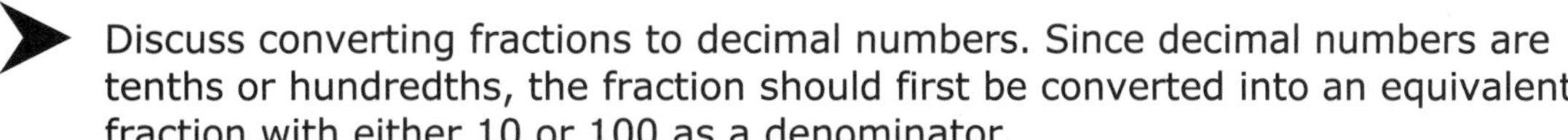

Discuss converting fractions to decimal numbers. Since decimal numbers are tenths or hundredths, the fraction should first be converted into an equivalent fraction with either 10 or 100 as a denominator.

$$\frac{1}{2} = \frac{5}{10} = 0.5 \qquad \frac{1}{25} = \frac{4}{100} = 0.04$$

$$\frac{1}{4} = \frac{25}{100} = 0.25 \qquad \frac{1}{20} = \frac{5}{100} = 0.05$$

$$\frac{1}{5} = \frac{2}{10} = 0.2 \qquad \frac{1}{50} = \frac{2}{100} = 0.02$$

$$\frac{1}{10} = 0.1 \qquad \frac{3}{25} = \frac{3 \times 4}{25 \times 4} = \frac{12}{100} = 0.12$$

Learning Tasks 10-13, p. 17

10. (a) $\frac{1}{4}$ (b) $1\frac{21}{25}$

11. (a) $\frac{3}{50}$ (b) $\frac{7}{25}$ (c) $\frac{6}{25}$
(d) $2\frac{1}{20}$ (e) $3\frac{13}{20}$ (f) $4\frac{3}{4}$

12. (a) 6, 0.6 (b) 45, 0.45

13. (a) 0.75 (b) 0.35 (c) 0.32
(d) 1.5 (e) 2.4 (f) 3.54

Review factors of 10 and 100 so that it is easy to determine the number that the numerator and denominator has to be multiplied by to get an equivalent fraction with a denominator of 10 or 100. Your student should be able to easily supply the number in the blanks for the following:

2 x ______ = 10
5 x ______ = 10
4 x ______ = 100
20 x ______ = 100
25 x ______ = 100
50 x ______ = 100

Your student may develop a "short-cut" method for mentally finding the decimal number equivalent of fractions with a denominator that is a factor of 100. We can simply think of the other factor and multiply the numerator by it.

For example, for $\frac{3}{5}$, we can think "2", (since 2 x 5 = 10) and multiply that by 3. There is 1 decimal number place (the product was 10), so the decimal number is 0.6. With $\frac{7}{20}$, we can think "5" (since 20 x 5 = 100) and multiply that by 7. There are 2 decimal number places (since the product was 100), so the decimal number equivalent is 0.35

There is additional practice in Mental Math 1

Workbook Exercise 8

(5) Comparing Hundredths (pp. 18-19)

- Compare and order numbers of up to two decimal number places.

Use **fraction squares** to compare the decimal numbers 0.25 and 0.3. Ask which is larger. 0.3 is larger. Line up the two numbers:

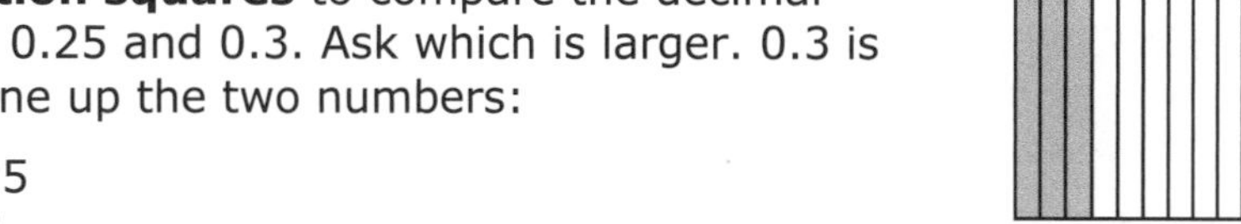

0.25
0.3

0.3 is larger because it has a 3 in the tenths place whereas 0.25 has only a 2 in the tenths place. When we compare decimal numbers, we need to compare the digits in each place value, not the total number of digits. 0.3 is equivalent to 0.30 ($\frac{3}{10} = \frac{30}{100}$) so we can add a 0 to the end of a decimal number to get the same number of digits, if that makes them easier to compare.

Write the following numbers and have your student put them in order.

12.3, 10.3, 12.25, 10.25, 10.03

First, we compare the whole number part. If they are the same, then we compare the tenths digit. If they are the same, then we compare the hundredths digit. The correct order is

10.03, 10.25, 10.3, 12.25, 12.3

Learning Tasks 14-17, pp. 18-19

14. (a) 2.9 (b) 1.68
15. (a) 562.41 (b) 89.67
16. (a) 42.6 (b) 2.5 (c) 32.6
17. (a) 2.2, 2.02, 0.2, 0.02
    (b) 80.7, 74.5, 7.8, 7.45

Highest number

Material: **Number discs** in a bag (100's, 10's, 1's, 0.1's and 0.01's.

Procedure: Each player draws 10 discs, and writes the number formed. The player with the greatest number gets a point. The winner is the one who gets 10 points (or some other target number) first.

Workbook Exercise 9

(6) Add or Subtract Tenths or Hundredths (p. 19)

- Add or subtract tenths or hundredths from 2-place decimal numbers.
- Find pairs of hundredths whose sum is 1.

In *Primary Mathematics 2B,* the student learned how to "make a 100". This was extended to making change for a dollar. Two strategies were taught for making 100 with a given number.

One method for making 100 is to count on, either first counting by ones to the next ten then by tens to 100, or counting on by tens to a number between 90 and 100, then the remaining 1's:

$$53 \xrightarrow{+7} 60 \xrightarrow{+40} 100$$

$$53 \xrightarrow{+40} 93 \xrightarrow{+7} 100$$

53 + **47** = 100

The second strategy is to use the knowledge that 100 is 9 tens and 10 ones to find the answer.

53 + ____ = 100

	5 tens	3 ones		5 tens	3 ones
+	? tens	? ones	+	**4** tens	**7** ones
	9 tens	10 ones		9 tens	10 ones

53 + **47** = 100

The student can use these strategies to find pairs of hundredths that "make 1."

Use **number discs** (1's, 0.1's, 0.01's) or base-10 blocks (flats as 1's, rods as 0.1's, and cubes as 0.01's), a **place-value chart**, and **two number cubes**. Label one number cubes (or put masking tape on each side if using regular dice) with 0.1, 0.2, 0.3, 0.01, 0.02, 0.03. Label the other number cube with three +'s and three –'s. Or, use eighteen index cards and make 3 cards each saying + 0.1, -0.1, + 0.2, - 0.2, + 0.3, - 0.3. Shuffle, turn over, and draw one at a time rather than throwing the number cube.

Put five 1's, five 0.1's, and five 0.01's on the place-value chart. Write the number 5.55. Your student throws both number cubes, and then adds or subtracts the number thrown by adding or removing discs. Rename as necessary. Write the equation each time. For example, he throws 0.02 and **–**. He removes two 0.1 discs and writes

5.55 - 0.02 = 5.53

If 5.92 is on the chart, and he throws a 0.2 and +, he must add two 0.1 discs. He must "make a 1" with one of the new 0.1 discs and the nine 0.1's on the board by removing the nine on the chart and putting a 1-disc in the 1's column. He then puts the other 0.1-disc in the 0.1 column.

5.92 + 0.2 = 6.12

If 4.42 is on the chart, and he throws 0.03 and **–**, he must subtract three 0.01-discs. He can rename a 0.1-disc as ten 0.01's and take away 3 of the resulting 12. Or he can take away 0.03 by taking away from a 0.1-disc replacing the 0.1-disc with seven 0.01 discs (0.1 – 0.03 = 0.07). He adds these to the two he already has; there are 9 0.01 discs now. He writes

4.42 – 0.03 = 4.39

➤ This next activity is similar to the one above, but uses larger numbers. Use **number discs** (10's, 1's, 0.1's, 0.01's), a **place-value chart**, and **three number cubes**. Use one as a regular number cube, with the numbers 1, 2, 3, 4, 5, and 6. Label the other number cube with three +'s and three –'s. Label the last number cube with two 1's, two 0.1's and two 0.01's. Put five 1's, five 0.1's, and five 0.01's on the place-value chart. Write the number 5.55. Your student throws all three number cubes and adds or subtracts the corresponding number of ones, tenths, or hundredths using the number discs and place-value chart, regrouping as necessary. He must write the equation. For example, he throws 5, 0.1's, and +. He must add five tenths, or 0.5.

5.55 + 0.5 = 6.05

➤ Repeat either of the two activities above, but do not use number discs or place-value chart. Your student just writes the equation. Students who have done the earlier levels of *Primary Mathematics* should be able to write the equation horizontally and do the addition or subtraction mentally. If not, save this activity for the next unit.

Learning Tasks 18-23, p. 19

18. (a) 412.44 (b) 412.24

19. (a) 123.49 (b) 123.47

20. (a) 5.17 (b) 28.60

21. (a) 86.63 (b) 24.85 (c) 4.89
    (d) 54.22 (e) 6.20 (f) 3.43

22. (a) 0.54 (b) 0.04

23. 0.18

 If necessary, review the strategies for "making 100."

Use two number cubes. One is labeled with 1, 2, 3, 4, 5, and 6. The other is labeled with 0, 9, 8, 7, 6, and 5. The student throws two number cubes and writes down a 2-digit decimal number. For example, he throws 5 and 3. He writes either 0.53 or 0.35. He then supplies the number that would "make 1" with the written number. For example:

0.53 + _____ = 1 0.47

More practice is given in Mental Math 2 and Mental Math 3.
Adding and subtracting tenths and hundredths will be reviewed and practiced again in the next unit and so does not have to be mastered here.

 **Workbook Exercise 10**

Part 3 Thousandths

(1) Thousandths (pp. 20-21)

- Read and write numbers to three decimal number places.
- Relate 3-place decimal numbers to thousandths.
- Express a fraction with a denominator of 1000 as a decimal number.
- Interpret numbers to three decimal number places in terms of hundreds, tens, ones, tenths, hundredths, and thousandths.
- Read scales in thousandths.

➤ Ask your student to write the number (not a fraction) for one tenth of 10, and name the number, then for one tenth of that, and name the number, then for one tenth of that, then for one tenth of that, and name the number. She may be able to write and name one thousandth on her own.

10	ten
1	one
0.1	one tenth
0.01	one hundredth
0.001	one thousandth

➤ Use **base-10 blocks**. Show your student the cube and flat from the base-10 set, and remind him that the flat is now 1, and the cube is one hundredth of it. If we divide the cube up into ten equal parts, how many parts would be in the flat. There would be 10 x 100 = 1000 parts in the flat. Each tiny part would be one thousandth, or $\frac{1}{1000}$, of the whole 1. It is one tenth of 0.01, so we write it one more place to the right, as 0.001. Emphasize the "th" sound in "thousand**th**."

➤ Use **number discs**. Show your student the ones for 0.001's. Ask him how many of them make up a 0.01 disc (10). How many make up a 0.1 disc? (100). How many make up a 1-disc? (1000). How many make up a 10-disc? (10,000).

Give him fifteen 0.001-discs and ask him to write the decimal number for 15 thousandths.

15 thousandths = 1 hundredth 5 thousandths = 0.015

Give him twelve 0.001-discs and twelve 0.01 discs and ask him to write the decimal number.

12 hundredths + 12 thousandths
= 1 tenth + 2 hundredths + 1 hundredth + 2 thousandths
= 0.132

Write the following fractions, and ask your student to write the decimal number:

$$\frac{2}{1000} = 0.002$$
$$\frac{20}{1000} = 0.020 = 0.02$$
$$\frac{200}{1000} = 0.200 = 0.2$$
$$\frac{2000}{1000} = 2.000 = 2$$

Note that the number of 0's after the decimal number does not change the number.

➤ Use **number discs** (1's, 0.1's, 0.01's, 0.001's) in a bag and a place-value chart. Have your student draw 10 or so of them (at least one 0.001-disc), and arrange them on a chart. (Or display a number on the chart.) Have him write it out as a sum of the values in each place and as a sum of fractions with 10, 100, or 1000 in the denominator. For example,

4 ones, 3 tenths, 2 hundredths, 2 thousandths
4.322
4 + 0.3 + 0.02 + 0.002
$$4 + \frac{3}{10} + \frac{2}{100} + \frac{2}{1000}$$

Ask him to read this number. It can be read as "four point three two two," or "four and three hundred twenty-two thousandths."

Then ask him to write the number that is 0.01 more, 0.01 less, 0.001 more, and 0.001 less than the given number.

Page 20
Learning Tasks 1-3, pp. 20-21

(a) 0.024 (b) 0.315 (c) 4.002

1. (a) five thousandths, 0.005
   (b) 2 - 20, 0 - 0, 4 - 0.4, 3 - 0.03
2. (a) 5.63 (b) 5.61 (c) 4.537 (d) 4.535
3. (a) 0.148 (b) 0.048 (c) 0.008

Workbook Exercise 11

(2) Comparing Thousandths (p. 21)

- Compare and order numbers of up to three decimal number places.
- Add or subtract hundredths or thousandths from numbers up to three decimal number places.

Learning Tasks 4-5, p. 21

Note that in comparing numbers we start with the highest place value. If the place value is missing, we can put a 0, as in 4.(a) where 42.54 and 42.326 are being compared. If necessary, have your student rewrite the numbers in tasks 4 and 6, one above the other, aligning the digits. Provide other examples if necessary.

4. (a) 42.54 (b) 63.182

5. (a) 3.02, 0.32, 0.302, 0.032
   (b) 2.628, 2.189, 2.139, 2.045

6. (a) 0.538, 0.83, 3.58, 5.8
   (b) 9.047, 9.067, 9.074, 9.076

➤ Use **number discs** (10's, 1's, 0.1's, 0.01's, 0.001's), **place-value chart**, and a **three number cubes**. Use one as a regular number cube, with the numbers 1, 2, 3, 4, 5, and 6. Label the other number cube with three +'s and three –'s. Label the last number cube with two 0.1's, two 0.01's, and two 0.001's. Put five 1's, five 0.1's, five 0.01's, and five 0.001's on the place-value chart. Write the number 5.555. Your student throws all three number cubes and adds or subtracts the corresponding number of ones, tenths, or hundredths using the number discs and place-value chart, regrouping as necessary. He must write the equation. For example, he throws 6, 0.001's, and +. He must add 0.006.

5.555 + 0.006 = 5.561

➤ Do the activity above, but do not use number discs or place-value chart. Your student just writes the equation. Students who have done the earlier levels of *Primary Mathematics* should be able to write the equation horizontally and do the addition or subtraction mentally. If this activity is too difficult, save it for the next unit.

Additional Practice is provided in Mental Math 4.

Workbook Exercise 12

(3) Thousandths and Fractions (p. 22)

- Express a number to three decimal number places as a fraction in its simplest form.
- Compare and order a mixture of decimal numbers and fractions.

 Ask your student to write 1.032 as a decimal number. She may write

$$1.032 = 1\frac{32}{1000}$$

Discuss how this can be simplified. It can be done all at once by dividing the numerator and denominator by 8, or in steps:

$$1.032 = 1\frac{32}{1000} = 1\frac{16}{500} = 1\frac{8}{250} = 1\frac{4}{125}$$

Now ask her to write 0.125 as a fraction in its simplest form.

$$0.125 = \frac{125}{1000} = \frac{1}{8}$$

This particular fraction is a good one to memorize. Knowing that 125 is $\frac{1}{8}$ of 1000, and 125 x 8 = 1000 will be useful later for mental math.

Since the factors of 1000 are 2, 4, 5, 8, 10, 20, 25, 40, 50, 100, 125, 200, 250, 500 all fractions in their simplest form of decimal numbers will have one of these in the denominator. One way of finding the equivalent fraction is to divide the numerator by 5 or 2 successively. If it cannot be divided by 5 or 2, it cannot be simplified any further.

 **Learning Tasks 7-10, p. 22**

7. $\frac{13}{250}$

8. (a) $0.5 = \frac{5}{10} = \mathbf{\frac{1}{2}}$

   (b) $0.08 = \frac{8}{100} = \mathbf{\frac{2}{25}}$

   (c) $0.024 = \frac{24}{1000} = \mathbf{\frac{3}{125}}$

   (d) $0.345 = \frac{345}{1000} = \mathbf{\frac{69}{200}}$

9. (a) $2\frac{9}{200}$

10. (a) $2.6 = 2\frac{6}{10} = \mathbf{2\frac{3}{5}}$

(b) $6.05 = 6\frac{5}{100} = \mathbf{6\frac{1}{20}}$

(c) $3.002 = 3\frac{2}{1000} = \mathbf{3\frac{1}{500}}$

(d) $2.408 = 2\frac{408}{1000} = \mathbf{2\frac{51}{125}}$

➤ Ask your student which is greater, $\frac{3}{5}$ or 0.8. To compare them, they need to both be expressed as decimal numbers, or both as fractions. Generally, it will be easier to convert the fraction to a decimal number. $\frac{3}{5}$ = 0.6, therefore 0.8 is larger.

Ask your student to put the following numbers in increasing order.

$3\frac{1}{5}$, 2.309, 30.29, $2\frac{39}{100}$

They could all converted to decimal numbers

3.2, 2.309, 30.29, 2.39

and then put in order. Here, though, it is not necessary to convert all of them. We can first look at the whole number parts and order them by the whole number. Then, only 2.309 and $2\frac{39}{100}$ need to be compared. The order is

2.309, $2\frac{39}{100}$, $3\frac{1}{5}$, 30.29

➤ You may wish to teach your student the terms *ascending* and *descending*. *Ascending* means to go up, so *ascending order* is from smallest to greatest. *Descending* means to go down, so *descending order* is from greatest to smallest.

 **Learning Task 11, p. 22**

11. (a) 0.6, 0.652, $\frac{4}{5}$, 2 ($\frac{4}{5}$ = 0.8)

(b) $\frac{7}{25}$, 0.35, $1\frac{3}{4}$, 7.231 ($\frac{7}{25}$ = 0.28, $1\frac{3}{4}$ = 1.75)

 **Workbook Exercise 13**

(4) Practice (pp. 23-24)

- Practice concepts involving decimal numbers.

Practice 1A, p. 23

1. (a) 0.6 (b) 6 (c) 0.06 (d) 0.006
2. (a) 4 (b) 7 (c) 0.08 (d) 0.004
3. (a) 5.509 (b) 2.819 (c) 13.52
4. (a) 0.72 (b) 3.78 (c) 5.8 (d) 8.04
5. (a) $0.08 = \frac{8}{100} = \mathbf{\frac{2}{25}}$ (b) $0.14 = \frac{14}{100} = \mathbf{\frac{7}{50}}$
   (c) $0.145 = \frac{145}{1000} = \mathbf{\frac{29}{200}}$ (d) $0.408 = \frac{408}{1000} = \mathbf{\frac{51}{125}}$
   (e) $3.6 = 3\frac{6}{10} = \mathbf{3\frac{3}{5}}$ (f) $1.12 = 1\frac{12}{100} = \mathbf{1\frac{3}{25}}$
   (g) $4.506 = 4\frac{506}{1000} = \mathbf{4\frac{253}{500}}$ (h) $2.006 = 2\frac{6}{1000} = \mathbf{2\frac{3}{500}}$
6. (a) 0.9 (b) 0.03 (c) 0.039 (d) 0.105
   (e) 1.7 (f) 2.18 (g) 3.007 (h) 0.999
7. (a) 0.07 (b) 0.2 (c) 2
   (d) 0.005 (e) 2 (f) 1000

Practice 1B, p. 24

1. (a) 0.008, 0.009, 0.08, 0.09
   (b) 3.025, 3.205, 3.25, 3.502
   (c) 4.386, 4.638, 4.683, 4.9
   (d) 9.392, 9.923, 9.932, 10
2. (a) 0.5 (b) 0.75 (c) 0.2
   (d) 3.8 (e) 6.25 (f) 4.6

US› 3. (a) = (b) >
(c) < (d) =
(e) > (f) >

3d› 3. (a) equal to (b) greater than
(c) less than (d) equal to
(e) greater than (f) greater than

4. (a) 1.703 (b) 0.085 (c) 5.069 (d) 10.052
5. (a) 0.248 (b) 0.792
   (c) 3.78 (d) 10.504
   (e) 7.009 (f) 9.803

Part 4 Rounding Off

(1) Round to a Whole Number (pp. 25-27)

➢ Round off decimal numbers to the nearest whole number.

In *Primary Mathematics 4A*, students learned to round whole numbers to the nearest 10 and to the nearest 100. This is useful for estimation. Here, the student will learn to round to the nearest whole number and to 1 decimal place. In unit 2, students will learn to divide decimal numbers by a whole number, and will encounter situations when the decimal part of the answer will go beyond thousandths. They will be asked to round their answers to one decimal number place. Rounding to a certain decimal place will become important in finding answers to a certain number of significant figures or precision in the secondary level.

Use the first two number lines on page a20 in the appendix or one of the blank number lines on page a21 (label each longer division with consecutive whole numbers) and ask your student to locate 1-place decimal numbers on the number line and give the whole number it is closest to. Note that if the tenths digit is 5, it is rounded up to the next whole number. Numbers up to 0.4 are rounded to 0.

Page 25
Learning Tasks 1-4, pp. 26-27

1. (a) 37
2. 6
3. 25
4. (a) 4 (b) 14 (c) 30
   (d) 5 (e) 16 (f) 19

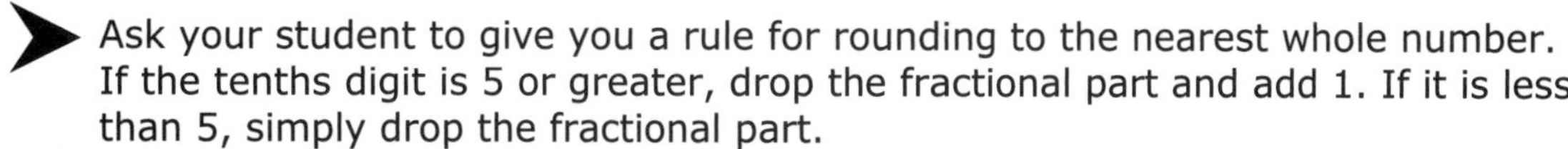

Ask your student to give you a rule for rounding to the nearest whole number. If the tenths digit is 5 or greater, drop the fractional part and add 1. If it is less than 5, simply drop the fractional part.

Ask your student for all the tenths that can be rounded to a certain whole number. For example, the numbers that can be rounded to 6 are

5.5, 5.6, 5.7, 5.8, 5.9, 6.1, 6.2, 6.3, 6.4

Workbook Exercise 14

(2) Round to One Decimal number Place (p. 27)

- Round off decimal numbers to one decimal number place.

Use the last number line on page a20 in the appendix or one of the blank number lines on page a21 (label each longer division with consecutive tenths) and ask your student to locate 2-place decimal numbers on the number line and give the tenth it is closest to. With the second number line, the division is 0.02. Then use the same with the first two number lines on page a20; the student will have to estimate where to locate the point. For example, he will have to place 3.08 just before the first division after 3. Note that if the hundredth digit is 5, it is rounded up to the next tenth. Decimal numbers up to 0.04 are rounded to 0.0, or 0.

Learning Tasks 5-7, p. 27

5. (a) 3 (b) 3.2
6. (a) 4.3 (b) 4.3 (c) 4.4
7. (a) 0.9 (b) 2.5 (c) 7.1
   (d) 11.0 (e) 18.0 (f) 24.6

Ask your student to give you a rule for rounding to one decimal number place. If the hundredths digit is 5 or greater, drop it and all digits following it and increase the tenth by 0.1. If it is less than 5, simply drop it and any digits following it.

Ask your student for all the hundredths that can be rounded to a certain tenth or whole number. For example, the numbers that can be rounded to 6.2 are

6.15, 6.16, 6.17, 6.18, 6.19, 6.21, 6.22, 6.23, 6.24

You may wish to extend this discussion to rounding to two decimal number places. Give your student some numbers to three decimal number places and ask her to round to two decimal number places. For example:

$345.382 \approx 345.38$
$45.905 \approx 45.91$

Workbook Exercise 15

Review

Review A, pp. 28-30

1. (a) 0.4 (b) 0.02 (c) 3 (d) 100

2. (a) 3.3, 3.03, 0.3, 0.03
   (b) 63.5, 6.4, 6.35, 5.63
   (c) 0.305, 0.29, 0.05, 0.009

3. (a) 30.06 (b) 16.82
   (c) 24.02 (d) 73.20

4. (a) 3 (b) 1 (c) 13
   (d) 10 (e) 4 (f) 5
   (g) 10 (h) 20

5. (a) 0.8 (b) 0.1 (c) 2.7
   (d) 8.1 (e) 10.9 (f) 19.1
   (g) 20.6 (h) 10.1

6. (a) 590 (b) 2830 (c) 12,100

7. (a) 5,700 (b) 13,800 (c) 45,100

8. (a) 4.05 (b) 4.15

9. (a) 6097 (b) 364 r2

10 (a) 5,700 (b) 10
   (c) 90,000 (d) 320

11. (a) $\frac{2}{3}$ (b) $\frac{1}{2}$

12. (a) $1\frac{7}{9}$ (b) $1\frac{1}{9}$ (c) $1\frac{3}{8}$
    (d) $3\frac{3}{10}$ (e) $4\frac{7}{10}$ (f) $5\frac{1}{4}$

13. (a) 1 (b) 1 (c) $3\frac{1}{2}$
    (d) $3\frac{1}{3}$ (e) $2\frac{2}{5}$ (f) $2\frac{2}{3}$

14. (a) 4.03 (b) 1.6 (c) 10.85 (d) 5.75

15. (a) $\frac{4}{5}$ (b) $1\frac{1}{4}$ (c) $4\frac{9}{20}$ (d) $6\frac{3}{50}$

16. (a) 10.4 11.4 12.7 (b) 2.4 3.4 4.8

17. (a) There are 4 more units of pencils than pens.
1 unit = 215
4 units = 215 x 4
= 860
There are **860** more pencils than pens.

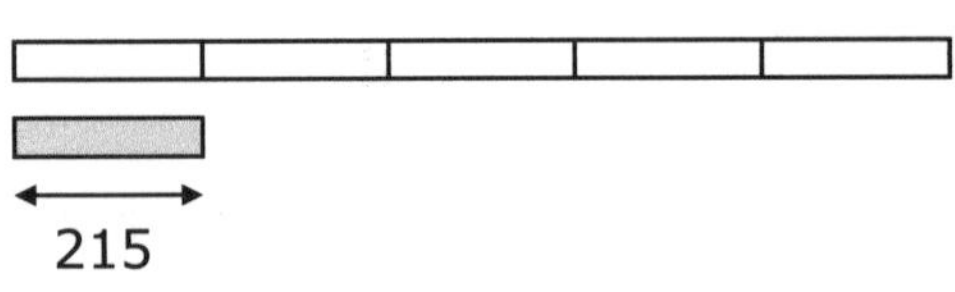

(b) 6 units - 215 x 6 = 1290 There are **1290** pens and pencils.

18. Total liters = 5 x $\frac{2}{5}$ = **2 liters**

19. She has 1 unit left.
4 units = \$20
1 unit = \$20 ÷ 4 = \$5
or: $\frac{3}{4}$ x \$20 = \$5
She had **\$5** left.

$20

?

20. 1 unit can't swim.
5 units = 40
1 unit = 40 ÷ 5 = 8
or: $\frac{1}{5}$ of the children can't swim. $\frac{1}{5}$ x 40 = 8
8 children cannot swim.

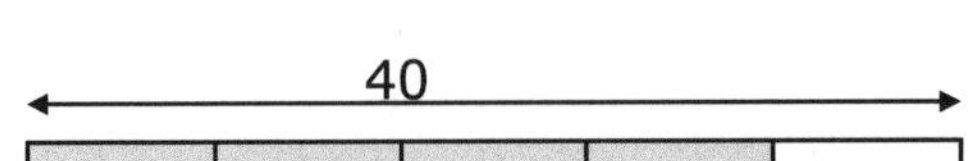

Workbook Reviews 1-3

Unit 2 – The Four Operations of Decimals

Part 1 – Addition and Subtraction

(1) Adding 1-Place Decimals (pp. 31-33)

- Add 1-place decimal numbers.

Students learned the formal algorithms for addition and subtraction of whole numbers in *Primary Mathematics 2A*, *3A* and *4A*. The formal algorithms for addition and subtraction of decimal numbers are the same as those for whole numbers. Numbers are aligned vertically, addition or subtraction done starting from the smallest place value, renaming the sum of each place value as necessary. Students should have a good understanding of place value and the basic addition and subtraction facts. In writing the problems vertically, students should take care to line up the decimal numbers correctly.

Students should be encouraged to add and subtract tenths and hundredths (decimal numbers with only one digit that is not 0) mentally, without rewriting the problem vertically. This was covered in the previous unit and is reviewed here. Various mental math techniques were covered in earlier guides. The same techniques apply with decimal numbers.

Page 31
Learning Tasks 1-5, pp. 32-33

In these problems, both the addends have only one non-zero digit. Students encountered problems of this sort already in Exercise 10; in this section students are shown how to align the numbers properly. Have your student align some of these problems, in preparation for problems with decimal numbers of more digits, but encourage him to normally answer these types of problems mentally.

(a) 0.9 (b) 0.5

1. (a) 0.7 (b) 0.07

4. (a) 0.8 (b) 1.3 (c) 1.2
   (d) 0.06 (e) 0.1 (f) 0.17

5. 7.3

If review of mental addition would be helpful, do the following activity. If review is not necessary, skip the next activity.

Use **one number cube**. Label it with the numbers 0.4, 0.5, 0.6, 0.7, 0.8, and 0.9. Write the number 5.5, or some other 2-digit 1-place decimal number. Your student throws the number cube and adds the corresponding number of tenths to the starting number. He continues until he reaches or passes a target number. This can be played as a game, with each player throwing the number cube during his or her turn and adding each time to the previous sum. The player who reaches the target number first wins.

Discuss the steps for adding numbers up to one decimal place. Illustrate the process with **number discs** and a **place-value chart**, if necessary.

4.5 + 8.7

Rewrite the problem vertically, aligning the digits.

$$\begin{array}{r} 4.5 \\ +\ 8.7 \\ \hline \end{array}$$

Add the tenths.
5 tenths + 7 tenths = 12 tenths
Rename 12 tenths as 1 one and 2 tenths.
Write the 2 in the tenths column and the 1 above the ones column.
Write the decimal point.

$$\begin{array}{r} {}^{1} \\ 4.5 \\ +\ 8.7 \\ \hline \mathbf{.2} \end{array}$$

Add the ones.
1 one + 4 ones + 8 ones = 13 ones = 1 ten and 3 ones.
Write 3 in the ones column and 1 in the tens column.

$$\begin{array}{r} {}^{1} \\ 4.5 \\ +\ 8.7 \\ \hline \mathbf{13}.2 \end{array}$$

Make sure your student lines up the digits correctly. If necessary, she can add 0's after the last digit following the decimal point to even out the number of digits.

$$\begin{array}{r} 3.\mathbf{0} \\ +\ 7.5 \\ \hline 10.5 \end{array}$$

Learning Tasks 6-7, p. 33

These problems can be rewritten vertically.

7. (a) 8.5 (b) 3.5 (c) 4.0
(d) 3.3 (e) 6.0 (f) 6.7

Students who have done earlier levels of *Primary Mathematics* may be able to do these problems without using the formal algorithm. Additional practice is given in Mental Math 5.

Workbook Exercises 16-17

(2) Adding 2-Place Decimals (pp. 34-35)

➤ Add 2-place decimals.

Learning Task 8, p. 34

8. (a) 1.32 (b) 0.51

In these problems, a tenth or a hundredth is being added to a 2-place decimal. Your student encountered problems of this sort already in Exercise 10. If more review is necessary, repeat the activities on pages 16 and 17 of this guide, using the number discs for 1's and 0.1's, and 0.01's. For additional practice, do the following activity, and/or use Mental Math 6. Encourage your student to answer these types of problems without rewriting the problem vertically. If review is not necessary, go on to the next activity.

➤ Use a **number cube**. Label it with the numbers 0.04, 0.05, 0.06, 0.07, 0.08, and 0.09. Write the number 5.55 or some other 3-digit 2-place decimal. Your student throws the number cube and adds the corresponding number of hundredths to the starting number. He continues until he reaches or passes a target number. This can be played as a game, with each player throwing the number cube during his or her turn and adding each time to the previous sum. The player who reaches the target number first wins.

➤ Discuss the steps for adding numbers of up to two decimal places. Illustrate the process with **number discs** and a **place-value chart**, if necessary.

4.56 + 8.78

Rewrite the problem vertically, aligning the digits.	$\begin{array}{r} 4.56 \\ +\ 8.78 \\ \hline \end{array}$
Add the hundredths. 6 hundredths + 8 hundredths = 14 hundredths Rename the 14 hundredths as 1 tenth and 4 hundredths. Write the 4 in the hundredths column and the 1 above the tenths column.	$\begin{array}{r} ^{1}\ \ \\ 4.56 \\ +\ 8.78 \\ \hline \mathbf{4} \end{array}$
Add the tenths. 1 tenth + 5 tenths + 7 tenths = 13 tenths Rename 13 tenths as 1 one and 3 tenths. Write the 3 in the tenths column and the 1 above the ones column. Write the decimal point.	$\begin{array}{r} ^{\mathbf{1}\ \ 1}\ \ \\ 4.56 \\ +\ 8.78 \\ \hline \mathbf{.3}4 \end{array}$

Add the ones.
1 one + 4 ones + 8 ones = 13 ones = 1 ten and 3 ones.
Write 3 in the ones column and 1 in the tens column.

$$\begin{array}{r} {\scriptstyle 1\ \ 1} \\ 4.56 \\ +\ \ 8.78 \\ \hline \mathbf{13}.34 \end{array}$$

Make sure your student lines up the digits correctly. If necessary, your student can add 0's after the last digit following the decimal point.

$$\begin{array}{r} 3.2\mathbf{0} \\ +\ \ 7.56 \\ \hline 10.76 \end{array}$$

Learning Tasks 9-14, pp. 34-35

Your student may be able to answer most of the problems in task 10 mentally. Have him rewrite the others vertically.

10. (a) 2.63 (b) 0.96 (c) 1.14
(d) 6.02 (e) 0.4 (f) 1.03
(g) 4.28 (h) 1.18 (i) 1.35
(j) 7.49 (k) 3.06 (l) 4.00

12. (a) 33.12 (b) 7.17

14. (a) 10; 9.76 (b) 7; 6.34
(c) 7; 7.18 (d) 6; 5.92
(e) 10; 9.43 (f) 13; 13.08

Workbook Exercises 18-19

(3) Subtracting Tenths (p. 36)

- Subtract tenths from numbers of up to two decimal places.

Learning Task 15, p. 36

15. (a) 0.6 (b) 0.8 (c) 2.8

Discuss these problems with your student. Use actual **number disks** or **base-10 blocks** (the flats are ones and the rods tenths) if necessary. In (a) we are simply subtracting tenths from tenths when there are enough tenths. In (b), and (c), there are no tenths, so we subtract from the 1. We can think of the tenth that will make a 1 with the tenth we are subtracting. Since 1 is 10 tenths, we can use the subtraction fact 10 – 2 = 8. We then decrease the ones by one. So in (c), we can look at the problem, see that we will have to subtract from a one, since there are no tenths, so we write down a 2, then a decimal point, then the difference between 10 tenths and 2 tenths.

3 – 0.2 = 2.8

2 1

0.8

Learning Task 16, p. 36

Here we do not have enough tenths to subtract 8 tenths. So we must subtract from a one. We will have one less one. We can subtract the tenth by recalling the subtraction fact 12 – 8 = 4, so twelve tenths – 8 tenths = 4 tenths, or we can subtract from the one (1 – 0.8 = 0.2) and add the difference to the tenths we already have.

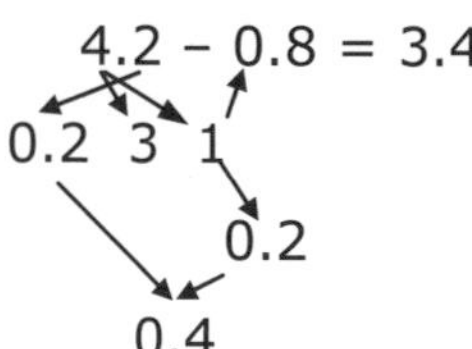

Learning Task 17, p. 36

Encourage your student to solve these mentally. Let him use the standard algorithm if necessary, rewriting the problem vertically and evening out the number of digits after the decimal point by adding 0's after the fractional part if necessary.

17. (a) 0.2 (b) 0.2 (c) 0.7
(d) 0.6 (e) 1.3 (f) 3.1
(g) 0.6 (h) 4.1 (i) 4.4
(j) 0.28 (k) 3.55 (l) 4.72

There is additional practice in Mental Math 7

Workbook Exercise 20

(4) Subtracting Hundredths (pp. 37-38)

- Subtract hundredths from hundredths, tenths, or ones.
- Subtract hundredths from numbers of up to two decimal places.

Students who have used previous levels of *Primary Mathematics* have learned to subtract 1-digit and 2-digit numbers mentally. The problems in this section can be done using similar strategies. Encourage your student to subtract tenths and hundredths (such as 0.3 or 0.03) mentally

Learning Tasks 18-19, p. 37

18. (a) 0.02 (b) 0.04 (c) 0.94
19. 0.77

Discuss these problems with your student, using actual number discs if necessary. In 18.(a), we are simply subtracting hundredths from hundredths. In 18.(b) we are subtracting hundredths from tenths. Since 1 tenth is 10 hundredths, we can use subtraction facts for tens, 10 – 6 = 4, so 10 hundredths – 6 hundredths = 4 hundredths.

Ask your student to also solve 0.3 – 0.06 here as well. We must subtract from one of the tenths, so we can write 0.2, then think of the fact for 10 – 6, and write 4 for the hundredths.

In both 18.(c) and 19 we can use the mental math techniques for making a 100. Since 1 is 100 hundredths, we can determine the number that makes 100 with the hundredth we are subtracting. In 18(c), 100 – 6 = 94, so 1 – 0.06 = 0.94. In 19, 100 – 23 = 77, so 1 – 0.23 = 0.77.

Ask your student to also solve 3 – 0.23. We need to take 0.23 from a 1, so we can think of this problem as 2 + 1 – 0.23 = 2.77

If your student needs further practice on making a 1 with hundredths, use the activity on p. 17 of this guide. Or use a **deck of cards** with the face cards removed and the tens made into 0's. Shuffle, have your student draw 2 cards, use them to make a hundredth, and supply the number that "makes 1" with it. For example, he draws a 7 and 4. He writes 0.74 and then 0.26. Or he writes 0.47 and then 0.53.

Learning Task 20, p. 37

20. (a) 0.07	(b) 0.47	(c) 3.47
(d) 0.06	(e) 0.26	(f) 2.26
(g) 0.93	(h) 1.93	(i) 3.91
(j) 0.55	(k) 2.55	(l) 3.14

There is additional practice in Mental Math 8.

Learning Task 21, p. 38

This learning task shows the formal algorithm for subtraction. Discuss it with your student. Use actual **number discs** or **base-10 blocks** to illustrate, if necessary.

Since 2 tenths is the same as 20 hundredths, we can even out the number of digits by appending 0's after the fractional part of the decimal number.

Discuss some mental strategies for subtracting hundredths.

In 3.24 – 0.06 we can write down the whole number part, 3, then subtract the fractional part mentally as 24 – 6 = 18, and writing the difference down after the decimal point. 3.24 – 0.06 = 3.18

5.5 – 0.08 can be solved by writing down 5 and the decimal point, mentally doing the subtraction 50 – 8 = 42, and writing the difference as the fractional part. 5.5 - 0.08 = 5.42

If there are no tenths, such as in 2.02 – 0.08, we can decrease the ones by 1, write the decimal point, and then mentally do the subtraction 102 – 8 = 94 and write the answer as the fractional part. 2.20 – 0.08 = 1.94.

Learning Task 22, p. 38

Your student can do these mentally or use the formal algorithm

22. (a) 3.23	(b) 3.47	(c) 4.16
(d) 4.74	(e) 6.13	(f) 6.41

There is additional practice in Mental Math 9.

Workbook Exercise 21

(5) Subtracting 1-Place Decimals (p. 38)

➢ Subtract 1-place decimal numbers.

Discuss the steps for subtracting numbers of up to one decimal place. Illustrate the process with **number discs** and a **place-value chart**, if necessary.

6.5 - 2.7

Rewrite the problem vertically, aligning the digits.

```
  6 . 5
- 2 . 7
```

There are not enough tenths. Rename 1 one as 10 tenths. Write a 1 next to the 5 tenths to show that you are now subtracting from 15 tenths. Cross out the 6 and write a 5 above to remind you that you only have 5 ones now. Subtract the tenths. (Or, 15 tenths - 7 tenths = 8 tenths
Write the 8 in the tenths column.
Write the decimal point.

```
  5
  6̸ . ¹5
- 2 . 7
    . 8
```

Subtract the ones.
5 ones - 2 ones = 3 ones.
Write 3 in the ones column.

```
  5
  6̸ . ¹5
- 2 . 7
  3 . 8
```

Make sure your student lines up the digits correctly. If necessary, your student can add 0's after the last digit following the decimal point to even out the 0's.

```
  1 3 . 0
-   7 . 5
    5 . 5
```

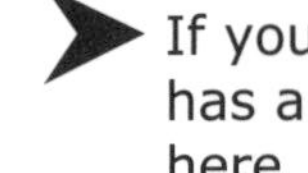

If your student is comfortable with subtracting 2-digit numbers mentally, and has a strong understanding of place value, she may apply the same strategies here. She may think of 6 – 2.7 as 60 – 27, subtract mentally, and insert the decimal point in the proper place. Or, she can do the "look ahead" strategy outlined in the earlier Home Instructor's Guides. Do not insist that she do these problems mentally.

Learning Tasks 23-24, p. 38

These problems can be rewritten vertically.

24. (a) 3.6 (b) 3.5 (c) 2.7
(d) 2.5 (e) 2.6 (f) 4.8

There is additional practice in Mental Math 10.

Workbook Exercise 22

(6) Subtracting 2-Place Decimals (p. 39)

➢ Subtract 2-place decimal numbers.

Discuss the steps for subtracting numbers of up to two decimal places. Illustrate the process with **number discs** and a **place-value chart**, if necessary.

4.32 - 2.78

Rewrite the problem vertically, aligning the digits.

```
  4 . 3 2
- 2 . 7 8
```

There are not enough hundredths. Rename 1 tenth as 10 tenths. Write a 1 next to the 2 hundredths to show that you are now subtracting from 12 hundredths. Cross out the 3 and write a 2 above to remind you that you only have 2 tenths now. Subtract the hundredths.
12 hundredths - 8 hundredths = 4 hundredths
Write the 4 in the hundredths column.

```
      2
  4 . 3̸ ¹2
- 2 . 7  8
         4
```

Rename a 1 as 10 tenths. Write a 1 next to the 2 above the tenths column to show that you now have 12 tenths, cross out the 4, and write a 3 above it to show that you have 3 ones now.
Subtract the tenths.
12 tenth – 7 tenths = 5 tenths.
Write the 5 in the tenths column.
Write the decimal point.

```
  3   12
  4̸ . 3̸ ¹2
+ 2 . 7  8
    . 5  4
```

Subtract the ones.
3 ones - 2 ones = 1 one.
Write 1 in the ones column.

```
  3   12
  4̸ . 3̸ ¹2
+ 2 . 7  8
  1 . 5  4
```

Make sure your student lines up the digits correctly. If necessary, your student can add 0's after the last digit following the decimal point to even out the 0's.

```
  10 . 3 0
+  7 . 5 6
   2 . 7 4
```

Do some problems where there are no hundredths or tenths. A one has to be renamed as 9 tenths and 10 hundredths.

$$\begin{array}{r} 8\ \ 9\ \ \ \\ \cancel{9}\,.\,\cancel{0}\,{}^{1}2 \\ -\ 3\,.\,4\,6 \\ \hline 5\,.\,5\,6 \end{array} \qquad \begin{array}{r} 9\ \ 9\ \ \ \\ \cancel{10}\,.\,\cancel{0}\,{}^{1}0 \\ -\ \ 3\,.\,5\,6 \\ \hline 6\,.\,4\,4 \end{array}$$

Some students may be able to do the second problem mentally. Subtract 3 from one less than the ones of the first number (10 – 1 – 3 = 6) and write the difference down for the ones, write a decimal point, "make 100" with the hundredths (100 - 56 = 44), and write that answer after the decimal point.

Learning Tasks 25-27, p. 39

These problems should be rewritten vertically.

26. (a) 3.74 (b) 0.31
    (c) 3.73 (d) 2.66

27. (a) 0.42 (b) 0.25 (c) 0.88
    (d) 3.4 (e) 3.49 (f) 3.55
    (g) 0.44 (h) 2.15 (i) 1.62
    (j) 1.55 (k) 3.44 (l) 0.95

Workbook Exercises 23-24

(7) Estimation, Other Mental Strategies (p. 40)

- Estimate to check the reasonableness of answers.
- Use mental strategies involving adding and subtracting decimal numbers close to 1.

Estimation helps reduce errors that may result from putting the decimal place in the wrong place, forgetting a step in the problem, or making some error in the math facts. It can help us see whether an answer is reasonable. It is also helpful to estimate when we need only an approximate answer, such as the approximate cost of some items we are buying. Estimation will be particularly useful in multiplication and division where there are more places for potential errors.

Encourage your student to estimate. If an answer he gives is unreasonable, ask him to estimate the answer and determine why it is unreasonable before correcting.

In *Primary Mathematics 2B*, students learned to add and subtract numbers close to 100. For example:

456 + 99 = 456 + 100 – 1 = 556 – 1 = 555
Count on 100, and back 1.

456 + 299 = 456 + 300 – 1 = 756 – 1 = 755
Count on 300, and back 1.

602 – 98 = 602 – 100 + 2 = 502 + 2 = 504
Count back 100, and on 2.

602 – 298 = 602 – 300 + 2 = 302 + 2 = 304
Count back 300, and on 2.

These strategies were also used in adding money. For example:

$4.55 + $1.95 = $6.50
Add $2, then take off 5¢.

$4.51 – $1.95 = $2.56
Subtract $2, and then add 5¢.

These strategies are extended to decimal numbers in this section.

Learning Tasks 28-39

29. (a) $8.67 + 7.2 \approx 9 + 7 = 16$; 15.87

    (b) $42.36 + 7.65 \approx 42 + 8 = 50$; 50.01
    (or $42.36 + 7.65 \approx 40 + 8 = 48$)

    (c) $20.81 + 18.76 \approx 20 + 19 = 39$; 39.57
    (or $20.81 + 18.76 \approx 20 + 20 = 40$)

30. (a) $7.23 - 4.6 \approx 7 - 5 = 2$; 2.63

    (b) $30.45 - 8.56 \approx 31 - 9 = 22$; 21.89
    (or $30.45 - 8.56 \approx 30 - 9 = 21$)

    (c) $52.36 - 24.82 \approx 52 - 25 = 27$; 27.54
    (or $52.36 - 24.82 \approx 50 - 20 = 30$)

Note that the accuracy of the estimation depends on the place value to which the numbers are rounded. Some student will round to a number with only one non-0 digit, or the highest place value. Other students who are more comfortable with mental math might round to the same place value for both. Allow your student to choose the degree of accuracy for their estimations. Generally, we want a quick estimation to see if the answer has the right number of place values.

Discuss mental strategies for adding numbers close to a whole. For example:

$6.29 + 3.98$

We can find an estimate from $6 + 4 = 10$.
We can easily get even closer to the correct answer with $6.29 + 4 = 10.29$.

If we add 4 to 6.29, we have added two hundredths too much.

We can easily go from this estimate to an exact answer by taking off the two hundredths too much that we added:

$6.29 + 4.98 = 10.29 - 0.02 = 10.27$

$9.99 + 34.2$

It is easy to find a close estimate from $10 + 34.2 = 44.2$

Because 9.99 is only 0.01 less than 10, it is easy to get from the estimate to the actual answer by subtracting the extra hundredth:

$9.99 + 34.2 = 44.2 - 0.01 = 43.19$

9.45 – 4.97

We can find a close estimate from 9.45 – 5 = 4.45.

Since 4.97 is 3 hundredths less than 5, by subtracting 5 we have subtracted 3 hundredths too much, so we can easily find the exact answer by adding 0.03.

9.45 – 4.97 = 4.45 + 0.03 = 4.48

Learning Tasks 31 – 34, p. 40

31. 7.27
32. 9.98
33. 3.63
34. (a) 5.86 (b) 10.80 (c) 9.98
 (d) 3.53 (e) 2.04 (f) 4.11

There is additional practice in Mental Math 11.

Workbook Exercise 25

(8) Word Problems (pp. 41-42)

- Solve word problems involving addition and subtraction of decimal numbers.

Students learned to use the part-whole and comparison models to solve word problems involving addition and subtraction in *Primary Mathematics 3A*.

Part-whole model for addition and subtraction:

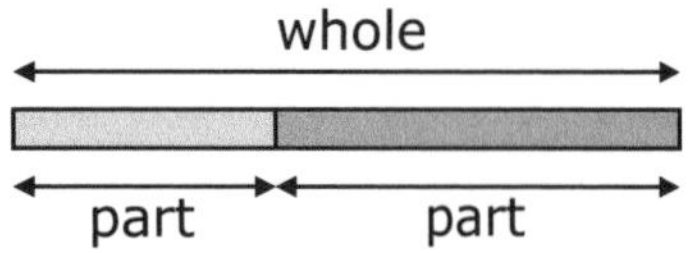

- Given two parts, we can find the whole by addition.
- Given a whole and a part, we can find the other part by subtraction.

Comparison model for addition and subtraction:

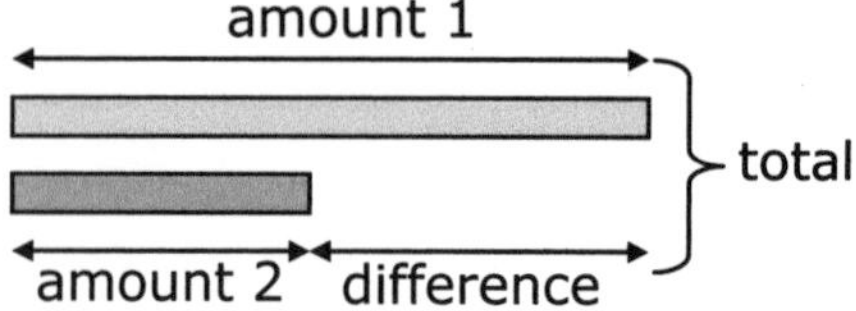

- Given amount 1 and 2, we can find the difference by subtraction.
- Given amount 2 and the difference, we can find amount 1 by addition.
- Given amount 1 and the difference, we can find amount 2 by subtraction.
- Once both amounts have been found, we can find the total by addition.
- Given the total and amount 1, we can find amount 2 by subtraction, and then the difference by subtraction.

Do not insist that your student draw the model if he can solve the problem without one.

Learning Tasks 35-37, pp. 41-42

35. $11.14
36. 5.1 m
37. $32.95

Workbook Exercises 26-27

(9) Practice (pp. 43-44)

➢ Practice adding and subtracting decimal numbers.

Practice 2A, p. 23

1. (a) 0.9 (b) 1.7 (c) 4.1
2. (a) 0.1 (b) 0.11 (c) 1.26
3. (a) 0.1 (b) 1.6 (c) 2.6
4. (a) 0.03 (b) 0.93 (c) 3.35
5. (a) 8.3 (b) 0.82 (c) 2.02
6. (a) 2.5 (b) 0.84 (c) 0.87
7. (a) 9, 8.85 (b) 8, 7.58 (c) 20, 20.04
   (d) 3, 2.80 (e) 4. 4.51 (f) 4, 3.64
8. Her height = 1.32 m – 0.07 m = **1.25 m**
9. Amount spent on meat = \$5.75 + \$7.50 = **\$13.25**
10. Amount he had at first = \$16.80 + \$3.60 = **\$20.40**
11. Amount of weight lost = 42.5 kg – 38.6 kg = **3.9 kg**
12. 15.3 s – 14.5 s = 0.8 s
    The person running fastest has smallest time.

US› **Fred** ran **0.8 s** faster.
3d› **Aziz** ran **0.8 s** faster.

Practice 2B, p. 44

1. (a) 48.68 (b) 19.43 (c) 40.02
2. (a) 28.6 (b) 17.31 (c) 19.98
3. (a) 13.33 (b) 22.23 (c) 4.89
4. (a) 36.65 (b) 11.05 (c) 10.61

US› 5. Weight of watermelon = 1.69 lb + 2.51 lb = 4.2 lb
Total weight = 1.69 lb + 4.2 lb = **5.89 lb**

3d› 5. Weight of watermelon = 1.69 kg + 2.51 kg = 4.2 kg
Total weight = 1.69 kg + 4.2 kg = **5.89 kg**

6. Amount used = 0.5 ℓ + 0.25 ℓ = 0.75 ℓ
   Amount left = 3 ℓ - 0.75 ℓ = **2.25 ℓ**
7. Distance jogged on Sunday = 5.85 km – 1.7 km = 4.15 km
   Total distance jogged = 5.85 km + 4.15 km = **10 km**

8. Total ribbon = 24.8 cm + 12.6 cm + 18.4 cm = **55.8 cm**
9. Amount Lucy spent = $15 - $4.15 - $6.80 = **$4.05**
10. Total spent = $4.90 + $7.50 = $12.40
    Change = $15 - $12.40 = **$2.60**

Get 0

Material: A **number cube** or spinner labeled with 0.09, 0.08, 0.07, 0.06, 0.05, 0.04.

Procedure: Start with a number, such as 2. Players take turns rolling the number cube and subtracting the number rolled first from the starting number, then from each successive difference. Subtractions must be recorded. The player whose final difference is closest to 0 when at least one player at the end of around can no longer subtract the number rolled because the difference would be less than 0 wins.

Part 2 Multiplication

(1) Multiplication of Tenths and Hundredths (pp. 45-47)

- Multiply tenths by a 1-digit whole number.
- Multiply hundredths by a 1-digit whole number.

In *Primary Mathematics 3A* students learned the formal algorithm for multiplying a whole number by a 1-digit whole number. The formal algorithm will be extended to decimal numbers in this unit. Your student should know the basic multiplication facts well and have a good understanding of place value. Mental math strategies will also be applied in this unit.

Use **money**. Give your student 6 dimes. Ask her how many dimes she would have if the number of dimes were tripled, or multiplied by 3. She would have 18 dimes. Write

6 dimes x 3 = 18 dimes
60¢ x 3 = 180¢

Ask her how much money 18 dimes is in dollars and cents, and how we would write this with the $ sign instead of cents.

$0.60 x 3 = $1.80

Now give her 7 pennies and ask her how much money she would have if this were multiplied by 5. Write

7 pennies x 5 = 35 pennies
7¢ x 5 = 35¢

Ask her how to write this using the $ sign.

$0.07 x 5 = $0.35

Use **number discs** and a **place-value chart**. Give your student 12 tenths and have him set them out in a 3 by 4 array. There are 3 tenths in a row and 4 rows. Write

3 tenths x 4 = 12 tenths

Now ask him to put them on a place-value chart. Since only 9 can go in the tenths column, he must rename 10 tenths as 1 whole. Write

0.3 x 4 = 1.2

Repeat with hundredths instead:

0.03 x 4 = 0.12

Write:

$3\underline{000} \times 4 = 12\underline{000}$
$3\underline{00} \times 4 = 12\underline{00}$
$3\underline{0} \times 4 = 12\underline{0}$
$3 \times 4 = 12$
$0.\underline{3} \times 4 = 1.\underline{2}$
$0.\underline{03} \times 4 = 0.\underline{12}$

Since 3 ones x 4 = 12 ones, then 3 tenths x 4 = 12 tenths, and 3 hundredths x 4 = 12 hundredths, just as 3 thousands x 4 = 12 thousands, 3 hundreds x 4 = 12 hundreds, and 3 tens x 4 = 12 tens.

We can answer 0.3 x 4 by thinking of the answer to 3 x 4, and remember we are multiplying tenths by 4 so the answer is tenths. We move the decimal point over one place value. In 0.03 x 4, we move the decimal point over two place values to the left, since hundredths is two place values away from the whole.

Ask your student to answer the following:

0.8 x 5   0.08 x 5

8 x 5 = 40., so 0.8 x 5 = 4.0 = 4, and 0.08 x 5 = .40 = 0.4

Page 45
Learning Tasks 1-6, pp. 46-47

It is not necessary to rewrite #4 vertically. The vertical representation in #2.(a) and #3.(a) is given to emphasize renaming. Your student should be able to do these problems mentally.

1.2

1.	(a) 0.8	(b) 0.08	
2.	(a) 2.1	(b) 3.0	
3.	(a) 0.21	(b) 0.3	
4.	(a) 6	(b) 0.6	(c) 0.06
	(d) 28	(e) 2.8	(f) 0.28
	(g) 40	(h) 4	(i) 0.4
6.	(a) \$0.80	(b) \$4.20	(c) \$7.2

There is additional practice in <u>Mental Math 12</u>

Workbook Exercise 28

(2) Multiplication of Decimals I

- Multiply numbers to 1-decimal place by a 1-digit whole number.
- Use estimation to check the reasonableness of the answer.

Ask your student to solve the following problem:

24 x 6

Point out that this is 24 ones times 6.

Then ask your student to solve 2.4 x 6.

```
  2 4
x   6
1 4 4
```

Tell your student we can ignore the decimal point for a moment and solve this problem as if it were 24 wholes times 6. But since it is 24 tenths times 6, then the answer is 144 tenths. Ask her to write 144 tenths as a decimal number under the line.

```
  2 .4
x    6
1 4 .4
```

When multiplying a decimal number by a whole number, the decimal point in the given decimal number and the product must be aligned. We do not normally align the whole number.

```
  2 .4
x 6
1 4 .4
```

With this or another problem, discuss the steps, dealing with each digit's place value. Illustrate with number discs if necessary, similar to p. 48 of the text.

```
  1 6 .8
x      3
```

Multiply 8 tenths by 3.

8 tenths x 3 = 24 tenths = 2 ones + 4 tenths

Write down the 4 tenths. We do not yet know the total amount of wholes we will have, so we write 2 above the ones to remind us that we have two more ones. Write the decimal point.

```
      2
  1 6 .8
x      3
      .4
```

Multiply 6 ones by 3.

6 ones x 3 = 18 ones = 1 ten + 8 ones.

We already have 2 ones from multiplying the tenths. We add that to the ones we get from 6 x 3.

8 ones + 2 ones = 10 ones = 1 ten.

We now have another ten and no ones. We write the ones (0) below the line and the tens above the tens to remind us we have 2 tens from multiplying the ones.

```
    2 2
  1 6 .8
x      3
    0 .4
```

Multiply 1 ten by 3

1 ten x 3 = 3 tens.

We already have 2 tens from multiplying the ones. We add that to the 3 tens.

3 tens + 2 tens = 5 tens.

Write 5 below the line in the tens place.

```
    2 2
  1 6 .8
x      3
  5 0 .4
```

➤ Remind your student that we can determine whether the answer is reasonable by estimation. This helps us make sure the decimal point is in the right place.

$16.8 \times 3 \approx 20 \times 3 = 60$

Have your student do the following problems, estimating first, then finding the actual answer.

3.2 x 6	18	19.2
30.2 x 6	180	181.2
2.2 x 5	10	11
7.6 x 8	64	60.8
14.2 x 3	30	42.6
6.5 x 8	56	52

➤ If your student is comfortable with mental multiplication of a two digit number by a 1 digit number, she may also be able to multiply a 2-digit number containing a decimal point by a 1-digit whole number mentally. For example

$4.6 \times 2 = 4 \times 2 + 0.6 \times 2 = 8 + 1.2 = 9.2$

There is additional practice in Mental Math 13. However, do not require your student to solve these types of problems mentally.

 **Workbook Exercise 29**

(3) Multiplication of Decimals II (pp. 48-49)

- Multiply numbers to 2-decimal places by a 1-digit whole number.
- Use estimation to check the reasonableness of the answer.

Ask your student to solve the following problem:

234 x 6

Point out that this is 234 ones times 6

Then ask your student to solve 2.34 x 6

```
  2 3 4
x     6
1 4 0 4
```

Tell your student we can ignore the decimal point for a moment and solve this problem as if it were 234 ones times 6. But since it is 234 hundredths times 6, then the answer is 1404 hundredths. Ask her to write 1404 hundredths as a decimal number under the line.

```
  2 .3 4
x      6
1 4 .0 4
```

Remind your student that we align the decimal point in the given decimal number and the product, but we don't have to align the whole number that we are multiplying by.

Remind your student to use estimation to see if the answer makes sense. Since 2 x 6 = 12, 2.34 x 6 will be about 12. 1.404, 140.4, or 1404 are not sensible answers. A common error is to forget the decimal point.

Point out that when we multiply dollars and cents, we can think of the problem in terms of just cents, and then convert back to dollars and cents. Have him do the following problem. first estimating the product:

```
 $6.05 x 8  ——→     6 0 5 ¢
$6 x 8 ≈ 48       x     8
                  4 8 4 0 ¢  ——→   $4 8 .40
```

If this were 6.05 x 8, the answer would be 48.4, since we would not need to include any trailing 0's after the decimal point.

Learning Tasks 7-8, p. 48

Discuss the steps for multiplying 2-decmal place numbers by a 1-digit whole number. Use actual number discs if necessary.

Learning Tasks 9-14, p. 49

9.	(a) 12.9	(b) 1.04	(c) 12.48
	(d) 11.8	(e) 2.25	(f) 36.16
10.	(a) 124.2	(b) 260.8	
	(c) 414.09	(d) 180.81	
11.	(a) 37	(b) 102.06	(c) 289.56
	(d) 80.4	(e) 180.75	(f) 442
13.	(a) 20; 19.5	(b) 8; 5.76	(c) 180; 178.38
14.	(a) 8.2	(b) 117	(c) 292.05

Workbook Exercises 30-31

(4) Word Problems (pp. 50-51)

➢ Solve word problems involving multiplication of decimal numbers.

Students learned to use the concept of units with the part-whole and comparison models to solve word problems involving multiplication and division in *Primary Mathematics 3A*.

Part-whole model for multiplication and division:

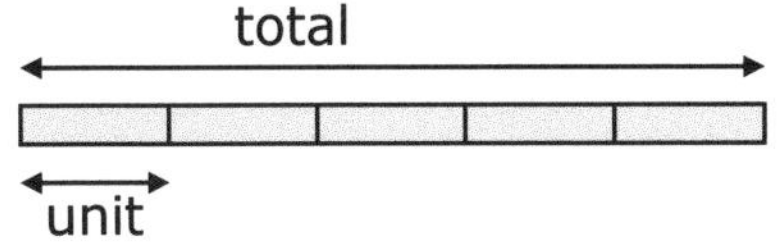

❖ Given the value of a unit and the number of units, we can find the total by multiplication.

Comparison model for multiplication and division:

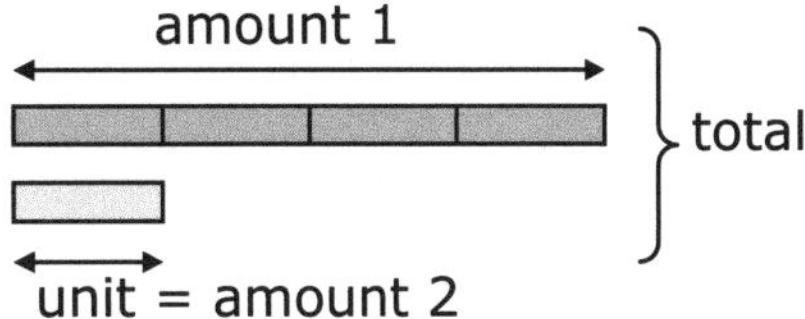

❖ Given the value of the unit and how many times as much amount 1 is compared to amount 2, we can find amount 1 by multiplication.

❖ We can then find the difference by multiplication or subtraction, and the total by multiplication or addition.

Combination of part-whole and comparison models:

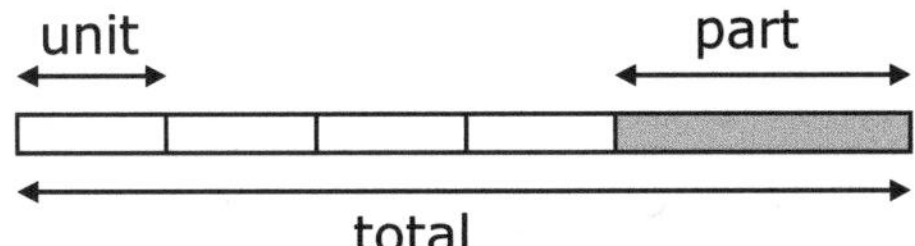

❖ Given the unit, the part, and the number of units, we can find the value of the total by mutliplication, and then addition.

❖ Given the unit, the number of units, and the total, we can find the value of the part by mutliplication, and then subtraction.

Do not insist that your student draw the model if he can solve the problem without one.

Learning Tasks 15-18, pp. 50-51

15. **23.70**

    Point out to your student that each short bar is 1 unit.

    1 unit = \$3.95
    6 units = \$3.95 x 6 = \$23.70

16. **80.20**

US› Rachel's savings = 1 unit
US› Susan's savings = 4 units

3d› Meihua's savings = 1 unit
3d› Sumin's savings = 4 units

1 unit = $20.05
4 units = $20.05 x 4 = $80.20

US› Also ask how much more Susan saved than Rachel. She saved 3 more units.
3d› Also ask how much more Sumin saved than Meihua. She saved 3 more units.

3 units = $20.05 x 3 = $60.15
or: $80.20 - $20.05 = $60.15

How much did they save altogether? Altogether, there are 5 units.
5 units = $20.05 x 5 = $100.25
or: $80.20 + $20.05 = $100.25

17. **$18.20**

You may wish to guide your student in illustrating this problem with a model. We can show his total money as one long bar. We divide it up into 2 parts, the part he spent on stamps, and the part he has left. Since he bought 4 stamps, and we know the cost of each stamp, we can divide the part he spent on stamps into 4 equal units.

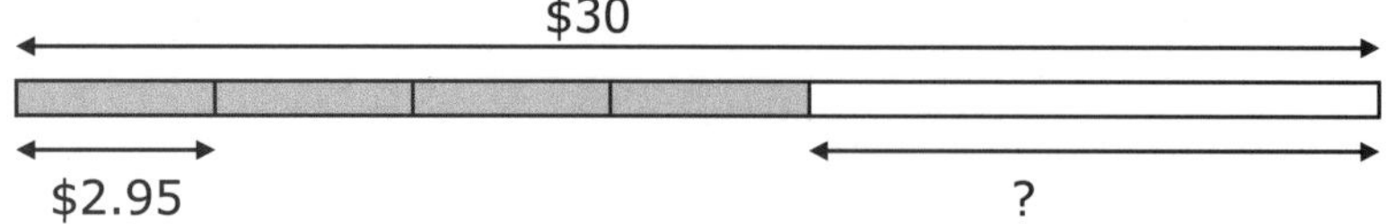

18. **21.4**

This can also be modeled. The total bar is how much material she bought. We can divide this up into two parts, the amount used for the curtains and the amount she had left. We know how much material she used for 1 curtain, and that there were 6 curtains. So we can divide the amount for the curtains into 6 equal units, each 3.15 m.

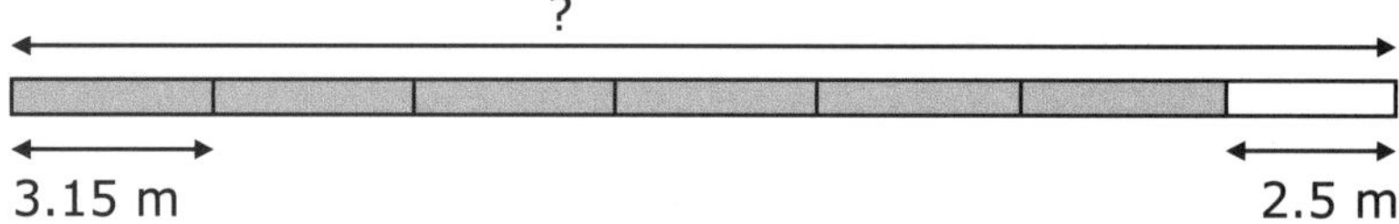

 **Workbook Exercises 32-33**

(5) Practice (p. 52)

➢ Practice multiplying decimal numbers.

Practice 2C, p. 52

1. (a) 8.6 (b) 11 (c) 2.28
2. (a) 6.23 (b) 4.52 (c) 4.14
3. (a) 5.3 (b) 3.5 (c) 1.85
4. (a) 1.52 (b) 3.17 (c) 2.85
5. (a) 3.6 (b) 5.6 (c) 1.86
6. (a) 1.35 (b) 6 (c) 19.3
7. (a) 18; 19.2 (b) 6, 7.44 (c) 20, 20.45
8. Difference = 1.5 m – 1.39 m = **0.11 m**

US› 9. Total sand used = 13.45 lb x 3
= **40.35 lb**

3d› 9. Total sand used = 13.45 kg x 3
= **40.35 kg**

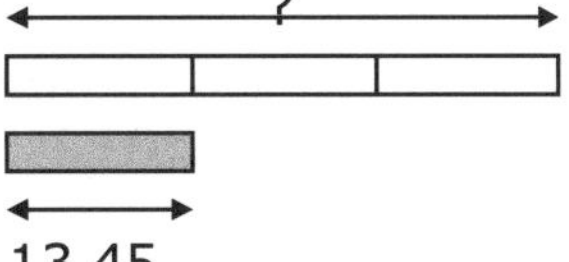

10. Total for spices = $0.85 x 4 = $3.40
Total for spices and cocoa = $3.40 + $3.75 = **$7.15**

11. Total paint = 1.46 ℓ + 0.8 ℓ = 2.26 ℓ
Paint left = 2.26 ℓ – 0.96 ℓ = **1.3 ℓ**

12. Cost of plants
= $2.35 x 5
= $11.75
Change
= $20 - $11.75
= **$8.25**

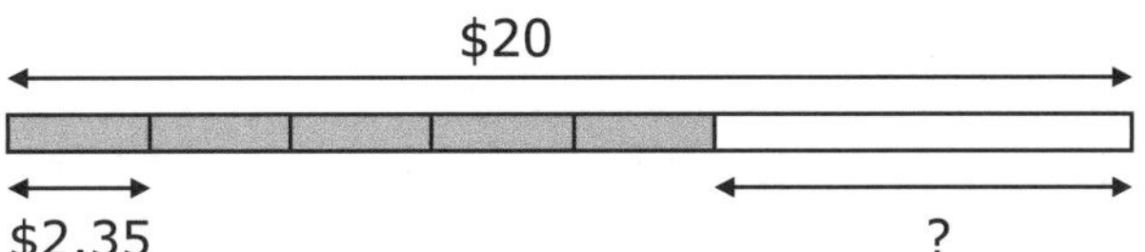

Part 3 Division

(1) Division of Decimals I (pp. 53-55)

➢ Divide a number of up to two decimal places by a 1-digit number where the quotient has only one non-zero digit.

In *Primary Mathematics 3A*, students learned the formal algorithm for dividing a whole number by a 1-digit whole number. The formal algorithm will be extended to decimal numbers in this unit. Your student should know the basic division facts well and have a good understanding of place value.

The terms dividend and divisor will be used in the discussions in this guide. You may want to teach these terms to your student, but they are not used in the course material. The dividend is the quantity to be divided, and the divisor is the quantity by which another quantity is to be divided.

$$\text{dividend} \div \text{divisor} = \text{quotient} \qquad \begin{array}{r} \text{quotient} \\ \text{divisor}\overline{)\text{dividend}} \end{array}$$

Use **number discs**, **money** (dollar bills, dimes, pennies) **or base-10 blocks** (flats as ones, rods as tenths, and cubes as hundredths). Give your student 12 ones and ask him to divide them into 4 equal groups. Do the same with tenths and hundredths. Write

12 ones ÷ 4 = 3 ones — $12 \div 4 = 3$
12 tenths ÷ 4 = 3 tenths — $1.2 \div 4 = 0.3$
12 hundredths ÷ 4 = 3 hundredths — $0.12 \div 4 = 0.03$

If we know $12 \div 4$, we can find $1.2 \div 4$ and $0.12 \div 4$

Rewrite these in vertical form. Point out that the decimal points of the quotient and the number being divided (the dividend) are aligned.

$$\begin{array}{r} 3 \\ 4\overline{)12} \\ \underline{12} \\ 0 \end{array} \qquad \begin{array}{r} 0.3 \\ 4\overline{)1.2} \\ \underline{1.2} \\ 0 \end{array} \qquad \begin{array}{r} 0.03 \\ 4\overline{)0.12} \\ \underline{0.12} \\ 0 \end{array}$$

Give your student 2 ones and ask him to divide them by 5. He can't do it without renaming it as 20 tenths. He should be able to recall the division fact 20 ÷ 5 and see that 2 ones is the same as 20 tenths.

$$2 \div 5 = 2.0 \div 5 = 0.4 \qquad \begin{array}{r} 0.5 \\ 5\overline{)2.0} \\ \underline{2.0} \\ 0 \end{array}$$

Similarly, ask him to divide 2 tenths by 5. He must trade in the tenths for hundredths in order to divide them into 5 equal groups.

$$0.2 \div 5 = 0.20 \div 5 = 0.04 \qquad \begin{array}{r} 0.04 \\ 5\overline{)0.20} \\ \underline{0.20} \\ 0 \end{array}$$

Page 53
Learning Tasks 1-6, pp. 54-55

Your student should be able to do tasks 4 and 6 mentally and does not need to rewrite these in the vertical format.

0.3

1. (a) 0.3 (b) 0.03
2. (a) 0.6 (b) 0.5
3. (a) 0.06 (b) 0.05
4. (a) 2 (b) 0.2 (c) 0.02
   (d) 5 (e) 0.5 (f) 0.05
   (g) 6 (h) 0.6 (i) 0.06
6. (a) 0.3 (b) 0.3 (c) 0.6

There is additional practice in Mental Math 14.

Workbook Exercise 34

(2) Division of Decimals II (p. 56)

- Divide a number of up to two decimal places by a 1-digit number where the dividend is less than one.

These problems and the ones in the next two sections can be illustrated with number discs and a place-value chart. A *general* procedure is given here for illustration (using a dividend greater than 1). A similar procedure may be used in this and the next few sections.

7.02 ÷ 3 (1) (1) (1) (1) (1) (1) (1) (0.01) (0.01)

Write the problem in the vertical format. Start with 7 1's and 2 0.01's. Divide the chart into 3 rows. First, divide the ones into 3 equal groups. Six are used, leaving one left over.

$$\begin{array}{r} 2 \\ 3\overline{)7.02} \\ \underline{6} \\ 1 \end{array}$$

(0.01) (0.01)

Ones	Tenths	Hundredths
(1) (1)		
(1) (1)		
(1) (1)		

(1)

Rename the left over one as 10 tenths. There are no other tenths. Divide them up into 3 equal groups. There are 3 0.1's in each group. Nine are used, 1 is left over.

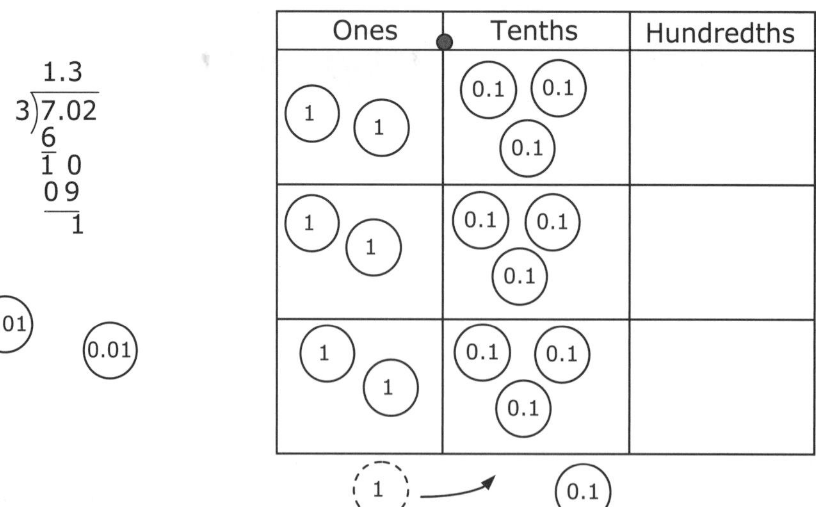

Rename the left over tenth as 10 hundredths. There are now 12 hundredths. Divide them into 3 equal groups. There are 4 0.01's in each group. 12 are used. 0 are left over.

```
   1.34
 3)7.02
   6
   1 0
   0 9
     12
     12
      0
```

Ones	Tenths	Hundredths
1 1	0.1 0.1 0.1	0.01 0.01 0.01 0.01
1 1	0.1 0.1 0.1	0.01 0.01 0.01 0.01
1 1	0.1 0.1 0.1	0.01 0.01 0.01 0.01

0.1

Learning Tasks 7-10.(c), p. 56

Illustrate these problems with number discs, money, or base-10 blocks, if necessary. Allow your student to work out the problems using manipulatives, if necessary.

8. (a) 0.13 (b) 0.21 (c) 0.11
   (d) 0.17 (e) 0.15 (f) 0.16

10. (a) 0.15 (b) 0.15 (c) 0.19

Workbook Exercise 35

(3) Division of Decimals III (pp. 56-57)

- Divide a number of up to two decimal places by a 1-digit number where the quotient has no more decimal places than the dividend.

Learning Tasks 10.(d)-14, pp. 56-57

Illustrate these problems with **number discs**, money, or base-10 blocks if necessary. Allow your student to work out the problems using manipulatives, if necessary.

10.	(d) 0.71	(e) 0.72	(f) 0.56
12.	(a) 1.32	(b) 1.03	(c) 2.43
14.	(a) 1.55	(b) 2.75	(c) 3.45

Workbook Exercise 36

(4) Division of Decimals IV (p. 58)

- Divide a number of up to two decimal places 2-places by a 1-digit number where decimal places have to be added to the dividend.

Up until now, except for problems involving decimal number multiples of single digits (e.g. 2 ÷ 5 = 2.0 ÷ 5 = 0.4) the student has not had to "extend" the decimal number to complete the division. They will be doing that in this section.

Learning Tasks 15-17, p. 58

Illustrate as much as necessary with **number discs**, money, or base-10 blocks. Allow your student to work out the problems using manipulatives, if necessary.

16. (a) 6.08 (b) 1.5

17. (a) 1.6 (b) 2.5 (c) 2.75
(d) 0.45 (e) 0.34 (f) 4.25

Workbook Exercise 37

(5) Estimation and Rounding (p. 59)

- Estimate to check whether an answer is reasonable.
- Round the quotient in a division problem to 1-decimal place.

Remind your student that when estimating a quotient, we round the number being divided (the dividend) to a multiple of the number we are dividing by (the divisor). For example, when we estimate

$$448 \div 7 \approx 420 \div 7 = 60$$

we round to the nearest multiply of 7. We do the same thing with decimal numbers:

$$4.48 \div 7 \approx 4.2 \div 7 = 0.6$$

Have your student find the actual value as well (0.64)

Learning Tasks 18-20, p. 59
3d› change 20(a) to 0.81 ÷ 3

20. (a) 0.81 ÷ 3 ≈ 0.9 ÷ 3 = **0.3; 0.27**
    (b) 7.12 ÷ 8 ≈ 7.2 ÷ 8 = **0.9; 0.89**
    (c) 46.35 ÷ 9 ≈ 45 ÷ 9 = **5; 5.15**

Do some of the following division problems with your student. He should not have trouble with the concept of extending the decimal place past thousandths. Continue the division process until he starts either noticing a pattern or sees that there is no pattern. 4 ÷ 9, 26 ÷ 3, 4 ÷ 7, 22 ÷ 7

```
    0.444         8.666        0.57142         3.14285
 9)4.000      3)26.000     7)4.00000     7)22.00000
   3 6          24            3 5            21
     40          2 0            50            1 0
     36          1 8            49              7
      40           20            10             30
      36           18             7             28
       4            20            30             20
                    18            28             14
                     2             20             60
                                   14             56
                                    6              40
                                                   35
                                                    5
```

Since these quotients go on forever without giving a remainder of 0 we can give an approximate answer by rounding to a certain number of decimal places. Even if the quotient did not go on forever, sometimes we only want an approximate answer and will round to a certain number of decimal places. We will be rounding to 1 decimal place. In order to do so, we have to continue the division to the second decimal place so that we can see whether the first decimal place needs to be rounded up or down. So we would find

$9 \div 4 = 0.44... \approx 0.4$
$26 \div 3 = 8.66... \approx 8.7$
$4 \div 7 = 0.57... \approx 0.6$
$22 \div 7 = 3.14 \approx 3.1$

The value of $9 \div 4$ is 0.4 correct to 1 decimal place.

Learning Tasks 21-23, p. 59

21. 2.3; 2.3
22. 19.6
23. (a) 0.2 (b) 0.6 (c) 0.6
    (d) 0.2 (e) 0.4 (f) 5.4

Optional Enrichment:
Have your student find the following values until she sees a pattern and can continue it:

$1 \div 9$
$2 \div 9$
$3 \div 9$
$4 \div 9$
$5 \div 9$
$6 \div 9$
$7 \div 9$
$8 \div 9$

According to the pattern, what would be the value of $9 \div 9$? (0.999...) Is this number the same as the number 1?

Workbook Exercise 38

(6) Word Problems (pp. 60-61)

➢ Solve word problems involving division of decimal numbers.

Students learned to use the concept of units with the part-whole and comparison models to solve word problems involving multiplication and division in *Primary Mathematics 3A*.

Part-whole model for multiplication and division:

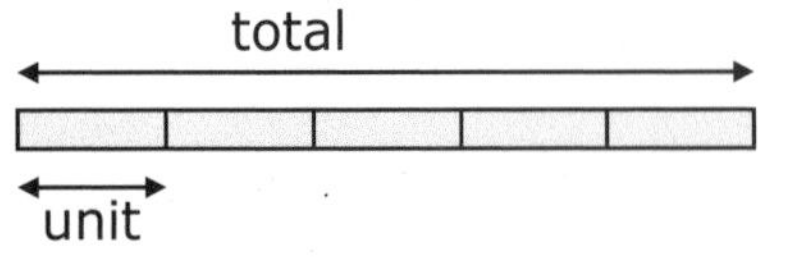

❖ Given the total and the number of units, we can find the value of a unit by division.

Comparison model for multiplication and division:

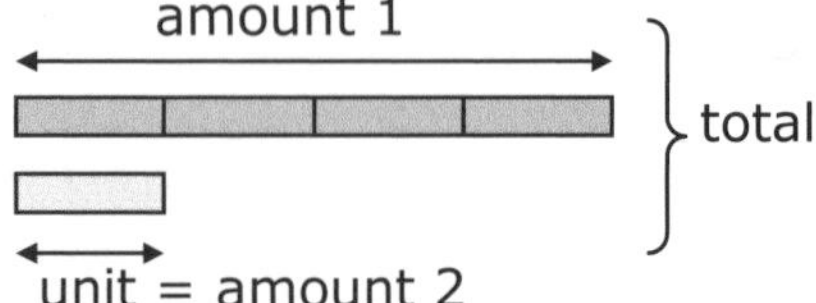

❖ Given amount 1 and how many times as much amount 1 is compared to amount 2, we can find amount 2 by division.

Combination of part-whole and comparison models:

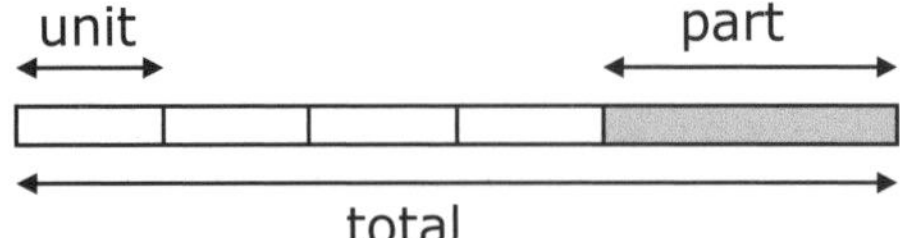

❖ Given the total, the part, and the number of units, we can find the value of the unit by subtraction, and then division.

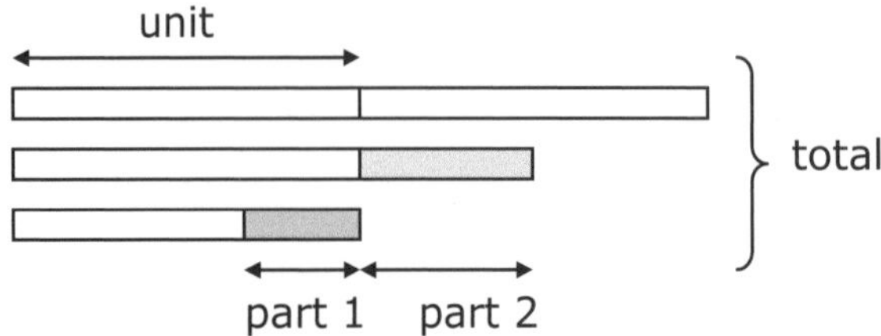

❖ Given the total and parts, subtract or add and then divide to find a unit. (3 units = total + part 1 – part 2)

Do not insist that your student draw the model if he can solve the problem without one.

Learning Tasks 24-27, pp. 60-61

24. **$3.20**

Point out that one short bar is 1 unit. In these problems we often have to first find the value of the unit.

5 units = $8
1 unit = $8 ÷ 5 = $1.60
2 units = $1.60 x 2 = $3.20

25. **$3.60**

Here, we also start by finding the value of a unit.

3 units = $5.40
1 unit = $5.40 ÷ 3 = $1.80

We can find how much more one has than the other by subtraction, as in the text, but we may also use multiplication.

2 units = $1.80 x 2 = $3.60

Also ask how much money they have altogether.

4 units = $1.80 x 4 = $7.20
or: $5.40 + $1.80 = $7.20

26. **0.95**

27. **1.08**

You may wish to guide your student in illustrating this problem with a diagram. Draw two bars the same length to represent the total flour. Divide one up into fourths for the amount of flour in each packet. Divide the other up into fifths for the amount of flour in each cake. Since the total length of the first bar is the same as the second, we find that first to find the size of the unit in the second bar.

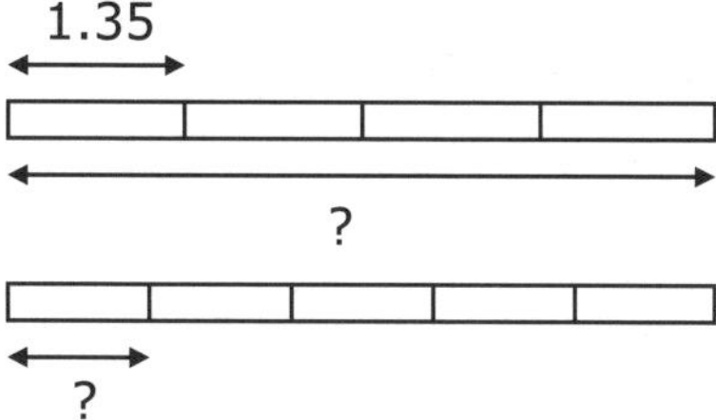

Workbook Exercises 39-40

(7) Practice (pp. 62-64)

- Practice multiplying and dividing decimal numbers.
- Practice word problems involving decimals.

Practice 2D, p. 62

1. (a) 32.8 (b) 15.87 (c) 26.32
2. (a) \$0.90 (b) \$16.20 (c) \$30.60
3. (a) 3.2 (b) 0.42 (c) 1.36
4. (a) \$0.15 (b) \$0.60 (c) \$0.85
5. (a) 36; 39.24 (b) 30; 31.5 (c) 14; 13.58
6. (a) 3; 2.95 (b) 4; 3.99 (c) 9; 8.76

US› 7. Amount in each bottle = 6 qt ÷ 4 = **1.5 qt**
3d› 7. Amount in each bottle = 6 ℓ ÷ 4 = **1.5 ℓ**

8. Weight of 6 liters = 1.25 kg x 6 = **7.5 kg**

US› 9. Length of each piece = 6.75 yd ÷ 5 = **1.35 yd**
3d› 9. Length of each piece = 6.75 m ÷ 5 = **1.35 m**

10. Total for string and beads = \$3 + \$1.40 = \$4.40
    Total for 4 hangers = \$4.40 x 4 = **\$17.60**
11. Weight of 6 bars = 2.34 kg – 0.06 kg = 2.28 kg
    Weight of 1 bar = 2.28 kg ÷ 6 = **0.38 kg**
12. Cost of comic = \$8.25 ÷ 3 = \$2.75
    Cost of book = \$2.75 x 2 = **\$5.50**
    or \$8.25 - \$2.75 = \$5.50

book
comic
\$8.25

Practice 2E, p. 63

1. Total paint = 5.5 ℓ x 8 = **44 ℓ**
2. Daughter's weight = 47.6 kg ÷ 4 = **11.9 kg**
3. Cost of robot = \$4.95 x 3 = **\$14.85**
4. Amount each girl paid = \$17.40 ÷ 3 = **\$5.80**
5. Cost of books = \$2.80 x 5 = \$14
   Change = \$20 - \$14 = **\$6**
6. Cost of 5 meters = \$50 - \$15.25 = \$34.75
   Cost of 1 meter = \$34.75 ÷ 5 = **\$6.95**

7. Amount saved for the first 4 days = $4.60 x 4 = $18.40
   Amount saved the last day = $25 - $18.40 = **$6.60**

8. Cost of tea = $0.65 x 3 = $1.95
   Cost of juice = $4.40 - $1.95 = **$2.45**

   $4.40
   $0.65

 **Practice 2F, p. 64**

1. Total cost = $2.50 x 3 = **$7.50**

2. Amount for each pillow case = 6.6 m ÷ 4 = **1.65 m**

3. Weight of 3 = 2.05 kg x 3 = 6.15 kg
   Weight of all 4 = 6.15 kg + 1.8 kg = **7.95 kg**

4. Cost of 6 plates = $1.45 x 6 = $8.70
   Cost of plates and pot = $8.70 + $5.65 = **$14.35**

5. Cost of lunch for Alice = $6.70 ÷ 2 = $3.35
   Amount of money she had left = $15.35 - $3.35 = **$12**

6. Cost of 3 pencils = $2.20 - $0.85
   = $1.35
   Cost of 1 pencil = $1.35 ÷ 3
   = **$0.45**

   $2.20
   $0.85

7. Amount used for bedrooms = 3.46 m x 3 = 10.38 m
   Total material used = 10.38 m + 4.25 m = **14.63**

8. Sale price of 1 kiwi = $2.20 ÷ 4 = $0.55
   Discount = $0.60 - $0.55 = **$0.05**

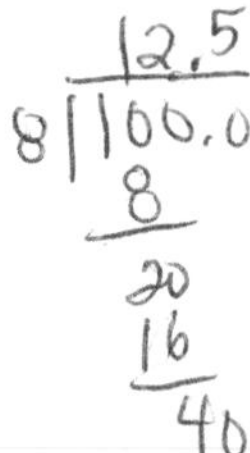

Review

Review B, pp. 65-67

1. (a) 124.66 (b) 124.57 (c) 124.46 (d) 124.55

US› 2. (a) > (b) < (c) < (d) =
3d› 2. (a) greater than (b) less than (c) less than (d) equal to

3. (a) 100 (b) 108
   (c) 10 (d) 1

4. (a) 100 (b) $35
   (c) 9 kg (d) 10 m

5. (a) 30; 29.4 (b) 63; 62.3
   (c) 20; 19.95 (d) 33; 32.97

6. (a) 8,000 (b) 80 (c) 8 (d) 80,000

7. 36

8. 456 ÷ 8 = **57**

9. (a) $1\frac{1}{12}$ (b) $\frac{8}{9}$
   (c) $1\frac{1}{3}$ (d) $1\frac{1}{2}$

10. (a) $\frac{2}{3}$ (b) $2\frac{4}{7}$
    (c) $\frac{3}{8}$ (d) $5\frac{5}{6}$

11. (a) $\frac{1}{12}, \frac{1}{3}, \frac{5}{6}$ (b) $1\frac{1}{4}, 1\frac{3}{4}, \frac{9}{4}$
    (c) $1\frac{3}{5}, 3, \frac{9}{2}$ (d) $2\frac{1}{5}, \frac{9}{4}, \frac{20}{6}$

12. $36,000

13. $77

14. (a) 6.7 (b) 14.3 (c) 4.9

15. Width = 50 cm^2 ÷ 10 cm = **5 cm**

US› 16. Length of one side = 36 in. ÷ 4 = **9 in.**
3d› 16. Length of one side = 36 cm ÷ 4 = **9 cm**

17 Total paid = $0.65 x 6 = **$3.90**

18 Length of 1 piece = 4.8 m ÷ 8 = **0.6 m**

19. $\frac{7}{10}$

20. Perimeter = $\frac{3}{5}$ km x 4 = $\frac{12}{5}$ km = $\mathbf{2\frac{2}{5}}$ **km**

21. Number of pieces she gave away $\frac{3}{8}$ x 16 = **6**

22. Number of girls = $\frac{3}{8}$ x 200 = **75**

23. Amount of water = $\frac{3}{4}\ell$ x 6 = $\frac{9}{2}\ell$ = $\mathbf{4\frac{1}{2}}$ $\boldsymbol{\ell}$

24. Amount saved in first 11 months = \$157 x 11 = \$1727
    Amount saved in 12th month = \$1800 - \$1727 = **\$73**

25. Cost of radio and watch = \$35.90 + \$28.50 = \$64.40
    Money he still needs = \$64. 40 - \$58.70 = **\$5.70**

Unit 3 - Measures

Part 1 - Multiplication

(1) Multiplication of Compound Units (pp. 68-69)

➢ Multiply length, weight, volume, and time in compound units.

Students learned to convert units within a measurement system (metric or US standard) and to add and subtract measures in compound units in *Primary Mathematics 3B*. In this section they will multiply measures in compound units.

If necessary, review conversion factors for measurement:

Length
- 1 m = 100 cm
- 1 km = 1000 m
- 1 yd = 3 ft
- 1 ft = 12 in.

Volume
- 1 ℓ = 1000 ml
- 1 gal = 4 qt
- 1 qt = 2 pt
- 1 qt = 4 c

Weight
- 1 kg = 1000 g
- 1 lb = 16 oz

Time
- 1 h = 60 min
- 1 min = 60 s

For review, ask your student to convert some measurements, such as

❖ 602 cm = ______ m ______ cm	6; 2
❖ 8 ft = _____ yd _____ ft	2; 2
❖ 3 yd = ______ in.	36
❖ 20 oz = ______ lb ______ oz	1; 4
❖ 2 kg = _______ g	2000
❖ 2048 ml = ______ ℓ _______ ml	2; 48
❖ 18 c = ______ gal ______ c	1; 2
❖ 12 qt = ______ gal	3
❖ 2 h = ______ min	120
❖ 185 min = ______ h ______ min	3; 5

If your student has trouble with these, consider going back to *the Primary Mathematics 3B* level and reviewing the units on measurements.

Page 68

Show your student that we can multiply the units separately.

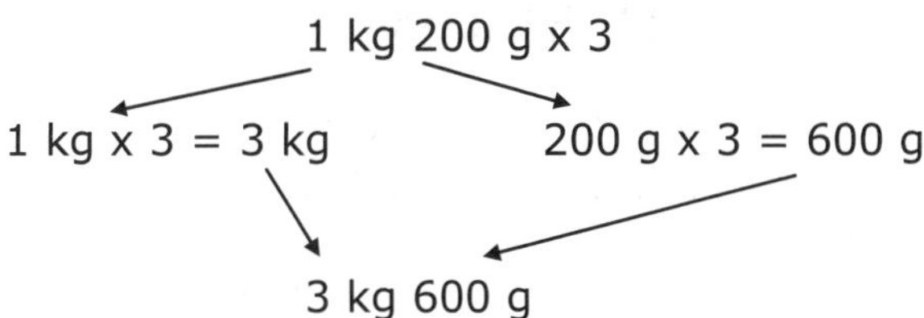

Learning Tasks 1, p. 69

After multiplying the units, then we carry out any necessary conversions.

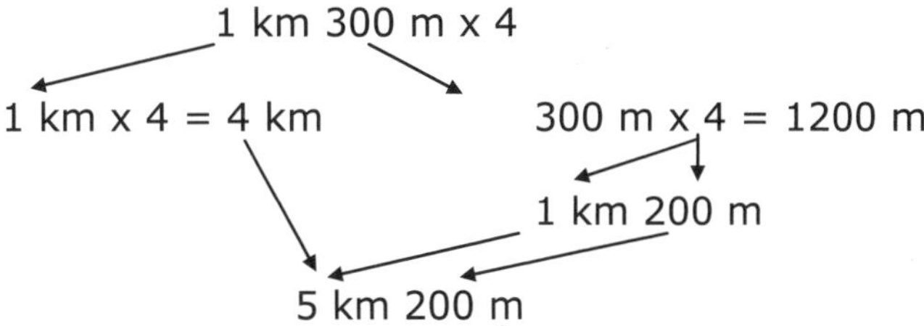

Learning Task 2, p. 69

2 ℓ 400 ml x 5 = (2 ℓ x 5) + (400 ml x 5)
= **10** ℓ + **2000** ml
= 10 ℓ + 2 ℓ
= **12** ℓ

Discuss some additional problems with your student, such as:

6 h 30 min x 6 = (6 h x 6) + (30 min x 6)
= 36 h + 3 h
= 39 h

This can be done either by 30 min x 6 = 180 min = 3 h, or by recognizing that 30 min x 2 = 1 h, so 30 min x 6 = 3 h.

2 ft 10 in. x 5 = (2 ft x 5) + (10 in. x 5)
= 10 ft + 50 in.
= 10 ft + 4 ft 2 in.
= 14 ft 2 in.

3 lb 8 oz x 4 = (3 lb x 4) + (8 oz x 4)
= 12 lb + 32 oz
= 12 lb + 2 lb
= 14 lb

16 gal 3 qt x 6 = (16 gal x 6) + (3 qt x 6)
= 96 gal + 18 qt
= 96 gal + 4 gal 2 qt
= 100 gal 2 qt

4 kg 201 g x 5 = (4 kg x 5) + (201 kg x 5)
= 20 kg 1005 g
= 21 kg 5 g

Exercise 3.1 (from appendix p. a16)

1. (a) 4 ℓ 230 ml x 9 = 36 ℓ + 2070 ml = **38 ℓ 70 ml**
   (b) 12 m 62 cm x 8 = 96 m 496 cm = **100 m 96 cm**
   (c) 3 ft 9 in. x 12 = 36 ft 108 in. = **45 ft**
   (d) 4 gal 3 c x 7 = 28 gal 21 c = **29 gal 5 c**
   (e) 8 min 15 s x 5 = 40 min 1 min 15 s = **41 min 15 s**
2. (a) Perimeter = 1 ft 4 in. x 4 = 4 ft 16 in. = **5 ft 4 in.**

   (b) Total weight = 1 lb 4 oz x 10 = 10 lb 40 oz = **12 lb 8 oz**

   (c) Length for shirts = 2 yd 4 in. x 4 = 8 yd 16 in. or **8 yd 1 ft 4 in.**
   Total length = 8 yd 16 in. + 1 yd 8 in. = 9 yd 24 in. = **9 yd 2 ft**

   (d) Time jogged Mon.-Sat. = 1 h 25 min x 6 = 6 h 150 min = 8 h 30 min
   Total time = 8 h 30 min + 40 min = **9 h 10 min**

Part 2 - Division

(1) Division of Compound Units (pp. 70-71)

➤ Divide length, weight, volume, and time in compound units.

Page 70

Discuss this problem with your student.

	5 m 20 cm ÷ 4
We divide the value for the larger measure first to get an answer in a whole number with a remainder.	5 m ÷ 4 = 1 m with remainder 1 m
4 meters have been divided. 1 meter and 20 centimeters remain. We convert the remainder and then divide.	1 m 20 cm = 120 cm 120 cm ÷ 4 = 30 cm
The final quotient is both parts.	**1 m 30 cm**

In this problem the larger unit was at least a multiple of the divisor. If it is not, then we convert and then divide. Give your student an example of this:

	3 yd 3 ft ÷ 4
First, convert the yards to feet	3 yd = 9 ft
Then, divide all the feet.	9 ft + 3 ft = 12 ft 12 ft ÷ 4 = 3 ft

At this stage, problems using US standard units will work out so that the smaller unit is a multiple of the divisor. But in some cases we can go to a smaller unit.

	3 yd 4 ft ÷ 4
Convert yards to feed and add it to the feet.	13 ft ÷ 4
We can have an answer that is a fraction of a foot, or convert to inches and try to divide.	3 ft remainder 1 ft 1 ft = 12 in. 12 in. ÷ 4 = 3 in. 3 yd 4 ft ÷ 4 = 3 ft 3 in.

In *Primary Mathematics 5A*, the student will learn to express the remainder as a fraction. At this level, the exercises won't require expressing the quotient as either a fraction or a decimal when dealing with measures.

Learning Tasks 1-3, p. 71

1. 5 kg ÷ 5 = 1 kg
   650 g ÷ 5 = 130 g 5 kg 650 g ÷ 5 = **1 kg 130 g**

2. 7 h ÷ 6 = 1 h remainder 1 h
   60 min + 30 min = 90 min
   90 min ÷ 6 = 15 min 7 h 30 min ÷ 6 = **1 h 15 min**

3. 3 ℓ = 3000 ml
   3000 ml + 200 ml = 3200 ml
   3200 ml ÷ 8 = 400 ml 3 ℓ 200 ml ÷ 8 = **400 ml**

➤ Optional: You may wish to show your student how these problems can be worked in a manner similar to the division algorithm. The remainder from division of the larger unit is converted and added to the smaller unit. This representation will be used in the solutions, but it is not necessary for your student to use it. For example:

```
   1 m  30 cm
4)5 m  20 cm
  4
  1             1 m + 20 cm
     120 cm  <-
     120
```

```
   1 h  15 min
6)7 h  30 min
  6
  1             1 h + 30 min
     90 min  <-
     90
```

➤ Discuss some additional problems:

10 min 12 s ÷ 6 = 1 min 42 s

```
   1 min 45 s
6)10 min 12 s
   6
   4
      252 s
      24
       12
       12
```

20 lb 2 oz ÷ 7 = 2 lb 14 oz

```
   2 lb  14 oz
7)20 lb   2 oz
  14
   6
       98 oz
       98
```

A piece of rope 22 ft long needs to be cut into 3 pieces. The second piece has to be twice as long as the first piece and the third piece has to be three times as long as the first piece. How long will the second piece be?

Total units = 6
1 unit = 22 ft ÷ 6 = 3 ft remainder 4 ft
4 ft = 48 in.
48 in. ÷ 6 = 8 in.
1 unit = 3 ft 8 in.
2 units = 3 ft 8 in. x 2 = 6 ft 16 in. = 7 ft 4 in.

The second piece will be 7 ft 4 in. long.

 **Workbook Exercise 41**

(2) Practice (p. 72)

- Practice adding, subtracting, multiplying, and dividing measures.

Practice 3A, p. 72

1. (a) 3 km 200 m x 5 = 15 km 1000 m = **16 km**
   (b) 4 ℓ 300 ml x 4 = 16 ℓ 1200 ml = **17 ℓ 200 ml**
   (c) 2 h 20 min x 5 = 10 h 100 min = **11 h 40 min**
   (d) 5 kg 200 g x 3 = 15 kg 600 g = **15 kg 600 g**
   (e) 6 m 20 cm x 6 = 36 m 120 cm = **37 m 20 cm**
   US› (f) 3 yd 2 ft x 7 = 21 yd 14 ft = **25 yd 2 ft**

2. (a) 2 ℓ 240 ml ÷ 2 = **1 ℓ 120 ml**

   (b)
   ```
        2 km  650 m
     2)5 km  300 m
       4
       1
             1300 m
             12
              100
              100
   ```

   (c) 1 h 30 min ÷ 5 = 90 min ÷ 5 = **18 min**

   (d)
   ```
        1 kg  500 g
     3)4 kg  500 g
       3
       1
             1500 g
             1500
   ```

   (e) 2 m 60 cm ÷ 4 = 260 cm ÷ 4 = **65 cm**

   US› (f)
   ```
        1 ft  5 in.
     3)4 ft  3 in.
       3
       1
             15 in.
             15
   ```

3. Total syrup = 1 ℓ 275 ml x 2 = **2 ℓ 550 ml**

4. Weight of beans in each bag = 3 kg 570 g ÷ 3 = **1 kg 190 g**

5. Total time = 3 h 30 min x 5 = 15 h 150 min = **17 h 30 min**

6. (a) Weight of watermelon = 1 kg 800 g x 3 = 3 kg 2400 g = **5 kg 400 g**
   (b) Total weight = 5 kg 400 g + 1 kg 800 g = **7 kg 200 g**

7. (a) Total hours in 6 days = 8 h 30 min x 6 = 48 h 180 min = **51 h**
   (b) Total pay for 6 days = 51 x $5 = **$255**

8. 3 units = 3 m 66 cm
   1 unit = 3 m 66 cm ÷ 3 = 1 m 22 cm
   2 units = 1 m 22 cm x 2 = 2 m 44 cm
   The longer piece was **2 m 44 cm** long.

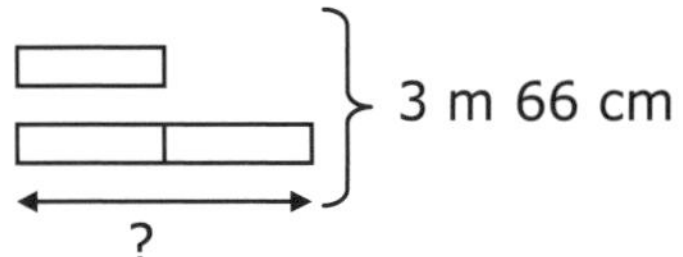

9. Total sugar = 1 kg 240 g + 1 kg 160 g = 2 kg 400 g
   Sugar for each cake = 2 kg 400 g ÷ 8 = 2400 g ÷ 8 = **300 g**

10. Total ribbon = 3 m 50 cm x 2 = 6 m 100 cm = 7 m
    Cost of ribbon = 7 x $4 = **$28**

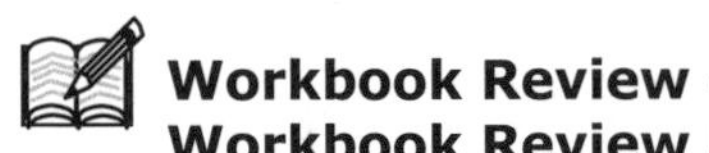
Workbook Review 4
Workbook Review 5

Unit 4 - Symmetry

Part 1 - Symmetric Figures

(1) Symmetric Figures (pp. 74-75)

- Identify symmetric figures.

Plane figures that have a line of symmetry are called symmetric figures. The line of symmetry divides the figure into two parts. Each part is a reflection of the other. When one part is flipped about the line of symmetry, it matches the other part.

At this point, students will be introduced to line symmetry only, not rotational symmetry. They will not be required to find the number of lines of symmetry of a figure.

Page 74
Learning Tasks 1-2, p. 75

Point out to your student that one side of a symmetric figure is a reflection of the other. Use a small **mirror** with a straight edge and place it on the line of symmetry on the figures in the text. Hold it carefully so that it is perpendicular to the page. The reflection of the one half of the figure in the mirror looks the same as the other half of the figure.

If you have a **math mirror**, put it on the lines of symmetry to show that one half of the figure fits exactly with the reflection seen in the mirror.

Cut a variety of figures out, as in learning task 2. Try to do so without creating a crease. Keep the page from which the figures were cut folded, but open the cut-out figure. Ask your student to match the cut-out with its source. Or your student can make the figures and challenge another to match them.

Workbook Exercise 42

(2) Lines of Symmetry (pp. 76-79)

- Identify and draw lines of symmetry.

If a given line is a line of symmetry, then a line drawn between a point on one side to its corresponding point on the other side is perpendicular to the line of symmetry and is bisected by the line of symmetry. So if there is a point along the edge or on an angle of the figure on one side of the line of symmetry that does not have a corresponding point on the other side along a line perpendicular to the line of symmetry and the same distance from the line of symmetry, then the line is not a line of symmetry. For example, though both sides of the line look the same in the diagram, the line is not a line of symmetry.

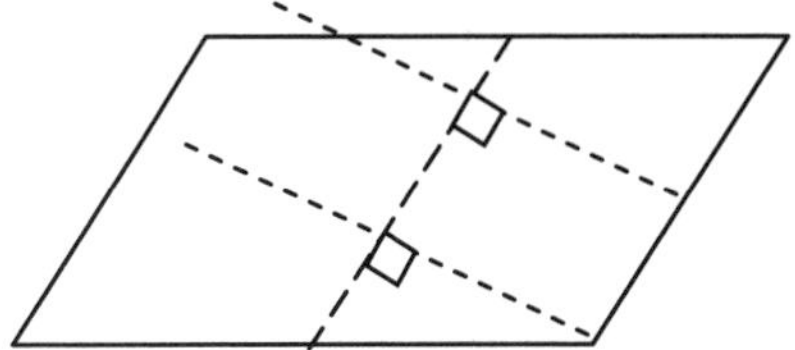

3d› If you are using the third edition of *Primary Mathematics 4B*, you will see in learning task 7 on p. 78 that in British English a quadrilateral with one pair of parallel sides is called a *trapezium*. In American English, it is called a *trapezoid*. (In British Englsh, a quadrilateral with no equal sides is called a *trapezoid*, whereas in American English it is called a *trapezium*.) This guide will use the American Engish term: a quadrilateral with only one pair of parallel sides is called a *trapezoid*.

Definitions and properties of isosceles and equilateral triangles, parallelograms, rhombuses, and trapezoids will be encountered again at later levels. It is not necessary to dwell on these at this point.

Learning Tasks 3-8, pp. 76-79

4. Any one of the following:

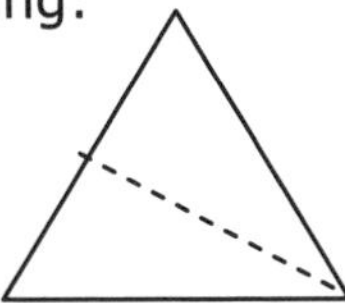

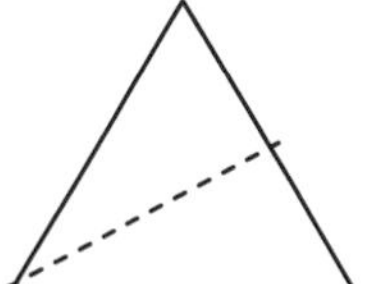

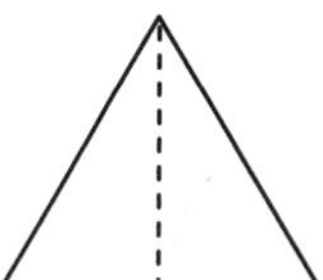

5. (c)
6. (a) no (b) yes
7. no
8. (a) yes (b) yes
   (c) no (d) yes

Workbook Exercise 43

(3) Completing Symmetric Figures (p. 79)

➢ Complete a symmetric figure with respect to a line of symmetry.

Learning Task 9, p. 79

You can redraw the figure on centimeter graph paper or other graph paper. Show your student that he can find where a corner or vertex of the figure should be by first drawing a perpendicular line from a vertex of the figure on one side to the line of symmetry, and then extending it the same distance on the other side. A second example with a slanted line is given below.

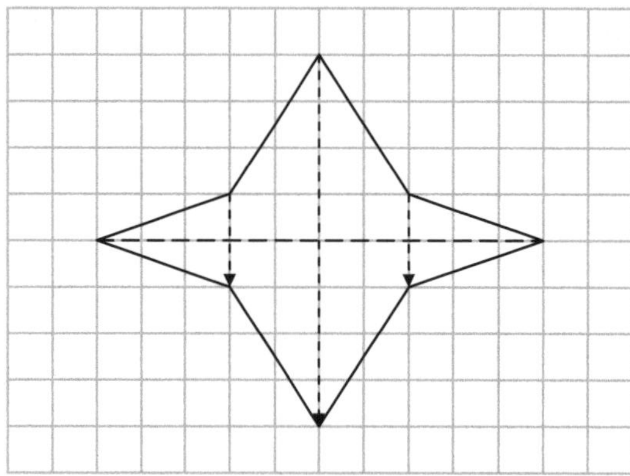

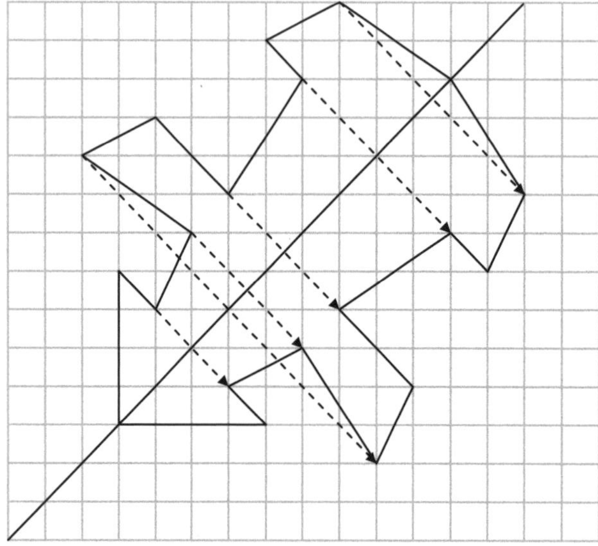

Workbook Exercise 44

There are some additional problems on Appendix p. a23.

Review

Review C, pp. 80-82

1. (a) 2 (b) 0.03
2. (a) 90,504 (b) 17,541
3. 2.69
4. (a) 80,300; 82,300 (b) 5.59, 6.09
5. (a) 14,680 (b) 30,083 (c) 9,900 (d) 89,301
6. (a) 7.03 (b) 4.9 (c) 2.41 (d) 3.602
7. (a) 14,058; 14,508; 41,058; 41,508
   (b) 0.96, 8.54, 24.3, 72
8. (a) 0.28 (b) 0.04
9. (a) A - 4490 B - 4540 C - 4620
   (b) P - 2.43 Q - 2.49 R - 2.54
10. 8.5
11. (a) Any 2 of these: 1, 3, 5, 9, 15, 45
    (b) 24, or 48, or 72...
12. (a) 10.41 (b) 15,336
13. Larger number = 3560 + 2790
    = **6350**

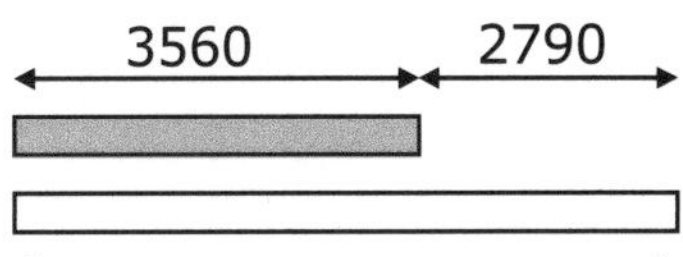

14. Length of red ribbon = 1242 ÷ 9
    = **138 US› in., 3d› cm**
15. Total money = $1.25 x 6 = **$7.50**
16. Additional water = 1.5 qt – 0.75 qt = **0.75 US› qt, 3d› ℓ**
17. Amount drunk in two weeks = 125 ml x 14 = 1750 ml = **1 ℓ 750 ml**
18. Total spent = $11.90 + $27.35 = $39.25
    Money left = $50 - $39.25 = **$10.75**
19. Money saved by brother = $20.35 + $16.85 = $37.20
    Total money saved = $20.35 + $37.20 = **$57.55**
20. Total paid by students = 18 x $3 = $54
    Amount Miss Chen paid = $72 - $54 = **$18**
21. Cost of 3 ovens = $2000 - $665 = $1335
    Cost of 1 oven = $1335 ÷ 3 = **$445**

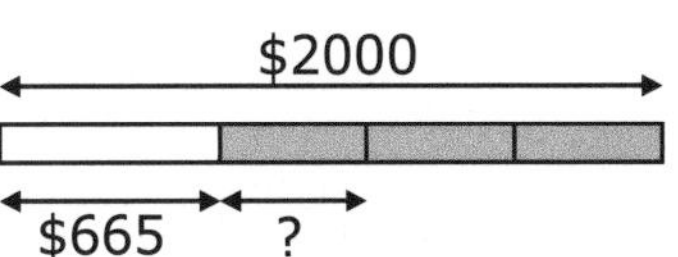

22. Total rent = $4500 x 2 = $9000
    Cost for each person = $9000 ÷ 4 = **$2250**

Review D, pp. 83-85

1. (a) 123.58, 132.85, 135.28, 251.83
   (b) 123.58 - 20; 132.8 – 2; 135.28 - 0.2; 251.83 - 200
   (c) 123.58

2. (a) 6 (b) 7

3. (a) 450.07 (b) 35.53 (c) 30.54 (d) 107.08

4. 42

5. (a) 30,000; 27,360
   (b) 9,000; 8,262
   (c) 32,000; 32,103

6. (a) $1\frac{4}{9}$ (b) $1\frac{3}{8}$ (c) $1\frac{2}{5}$
   (d) $\frac{1}{8}$ (e) 50 (f) $4\frac{1}{2}$

7. (a) $1\frac{9}{25}$ (b) 3.22

8. \$12.25

9. (a) Perimeter = 26 cm, Area = 22 cm^2
   (b) Perimeter = 62 cm, Area = 138 cm^2

10. (b) 327

US› 11. length + width = 42 in. ÷ 2 = 21 in.
width = 21 in. – 12 in. = **9 in.**

3d› 11. length + breadth = 42 cm ÷ 2 = 21 cm
breadth = 21 cm – 12 cm = **9 cm**

12. side = 5 m; Perimeter = 5 m x 4 = **20 m**

13. (a) 1 ℓ – 660 ml = **340 ml**
    (b) 1 kg – 256 g = **744 g**
    US› (c) 1 ft – 7 in. = **5 in.**

14. (a) 7 h 35 min (b) 10:05 p.m.

15. Cost of picture book = $\frac{2}{5}$ x \$34 = \$13.60
    Total spent = \$8.25 + \$13.60 = **\$21.85**

16. 2 units = \$14
    1 unit = \$14 ÷ 2 = \$7
    3 units = \$7 x 3 = \$21

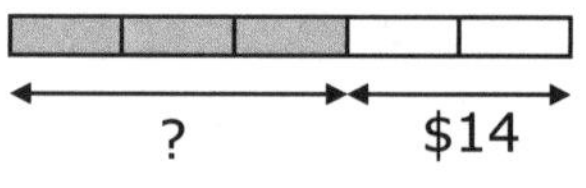

or $\frac{2}{5}$ of total = \$14

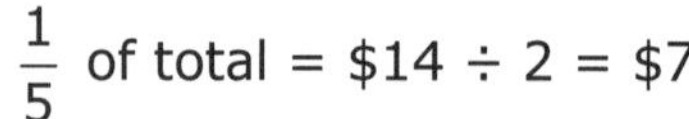
$\frac{1}{5}$ of total = \$14 ÷ 2 = \$7

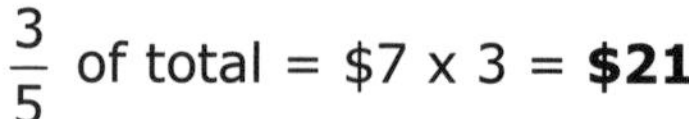
$\frac{3}{5}$ of total = \$7 x 3 = **\$21**

Unit 5 – Solid Figures

Part 1 – Identifying Solid Figures

(1) Building Solids from Cubes I (pp. 86-87)

- Interpret solids made up of cubes drawn on an isometric grid.
- Build solids from unit cubes.

In the exercises in this unit, you can use either multilink cubes or connect-a-cubes that allow you to connect cubes to each other to make 3-dimensinal structures. But you may also use cubes that do not connect to each other. In all of these exercises, assume that the figures can be constructed from blocks that do not link. Therefore hidden parts of the figures have to have blocks under other blocks so that no block is suspended in the air. The one exception is the figure of the "man" on appendix p. a26, which can only be constructed using multilink cubes.

Page 86

You may want to show your student how to draw a cube or other rectangular solid. There are several ways.

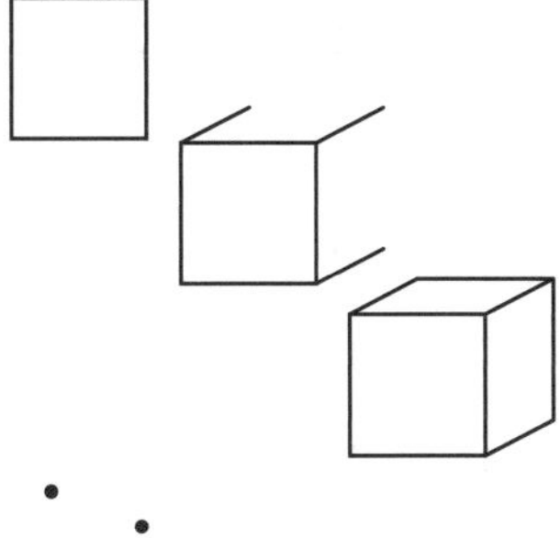

To draw one with a face front most, start with one face of the cube.

Draw parallel lines of equal length from three of the corners

Connect the ends of these lines with lines parallel to the face.

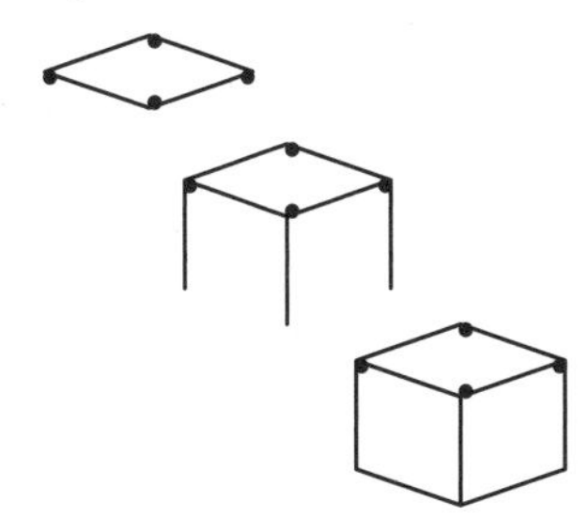

To draw one with an edge front most, draw two dots a ways apart, and two dots between them close together.

Connect the dots.

Draw parallel lines of the same length straight down from the two ends and the near corner.

Connect the ends of the lines.

Learning Tasks 1-3, p. 87

Use **multilink cubes** to build these solids from the pictures.
Point out that in 2.(a) one of the cubes is hidden, or can't be seen in the drawing. Since the top cube must be sitting on something, we assume that there is one in the back that we cannot see.

Enrichment

Your student may like to try drawing the solids she forms in 2.(b). If so, let her also build other solids and draw them on **isometric dot paper**. There is some isometric dot paper in the appendix. Practice drawing other constructions. Drawing the solid figures is not required at this level.

Workbook Exercise 45

(2) Building Solids from Cubes II (pp. 88-89)

- Build solids from unit cubes.
- Find the number of cubes in a solid drawn on isometric dot paper.

Learning Tasks 4-7, pp. 88-89

5.	A	5	B	6	C	9	D	9
6.	P	9	Q	8				
7.	A	12	B	10				

Appendix pp. a25-a26
Use **unit cubes** or **multilink cubes**. (Multilink cubes are necessary for page a 26.) Have your student build the figures and determine the number of cubes needed. He can try to determine the number of cubes needed before actually building the figure.

p. a25

A	24	B	14
C	10	D	11
E	20	F	48

p. a26

193

Workbook Exercise 46

(3) Making New Solids (p. 89)

- Visualize new solids formed by adding or taking away unit cubes from a solid drawn on isometric dot paper.

Learning Tasks 7-8, p. 89

Your student may be able to answer these without actually building the solids.

7. A has 12, B has 10; 2 were removed.
8. C has 4, D has 6; 2 were added.

Appendix p. a27
Have your student determine how many cubes were added or removed from the figures on the left to get the figures on the right. Use **unit cubes** or **multilink cubes** to build the figures.

A 6 removed
B 3 added
C 2 added (and 1 moved)

Enrichment

If your student likes drawing solids that she builds, she can build some, draw them on **isometric dot paper**, remove or add some cubes, and draw the new solid, and challenge you to determine how many cubes have been added or removed.

Workbook Exercise 47

Unit 6 – Volume

Part 1 – Cubic Units

(1) Cubic Units (pp. 90-92)

- Find the volume of a solid in cubic units.
- Visualize the size of cubic units in standard measurements.

Students were already finding volume as the number of cubes needed to make up a solid figure. Here, they are introduced to the term cubic units. Solids with different shapes have the same volume if they take up the same amount of total space, even if that space is arranged differently.

Page 90
Learning Tasks 1-2, pp. 90 – 91

1. 6
2. A. 5 B. 9 C. 18 D. 12

Most **multilink cubes** such as Connect-a-Cubes or Cube-a-Links are 2 cm long on each side (3/4 inch). If you have been using multilink cubes, show your student a unit cube from a base-10 set or other **1-cm cube**. Ask your student to measure the side. Tell your student that a cube with sides of 1 cm has a volume of 1 cubic centimeter. This is written as 1 cm^3. We can think of the little 3 as showing that we are measurement in 3 dimensions.

Learning Tasks 3-5, pp. 91-92

3. 3; 6
4. 32 cm^3
5. A. 4 cm^3 B. 12 cm^3
   C. 10 cm^3 D. 12 cm^3

Use both **multilink cubes** (2 cm on a side) and **1-cm cubes**. Put them next to each other so your student can compare the size. Ask him to measure the side of the multilink cube, and then to build a cube the same size using the 1-cm cubes. How many cubes are needed (8). What is the volume? 8 cm^3. Have your student build larger cubes or other shapes with the multilink cubes and find the volume in cubic centimeters. For example, if he builds a cube with 8 multilink cubes, the volume is 64 cm^3. Each multilink cube has a volume of 8 cm^3, so 8 of them have a volume of 64 cm^3.

Use the net in the appendix on p. a28. Cut it out and fold at the creases to make a cube. Ask your student to measure the side and tell you the volume. The volume is 1 cubic inch, or 1 $in.^3$. A volume of 1 $in.^3$ is as big as a cube with side 1 in.

Tape some paper together to make a similar net with 6 square feet and make a cube from it. Or use 12 strips of cardboard one foot long and use them to construct the edges of a cube. The volume is 1 cubic foot, or 1 ft^3. Save this for the next section.

Use masking tape to mark a square with side 1 meter on the floor with one side against the wall. Mark another square meter on the wall with the same edge as the square on the floor. Use meter sticks to mark two edges. Tell your student to imagine a cube from this. Its volume is 1 cubic meter, or 1 m^3.

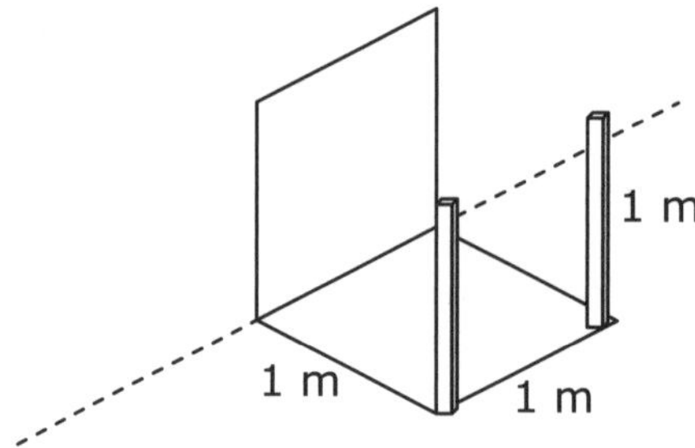

Workbook Exercises 48-49

Part 2 – Volume of a Cuboid

(1) Volume (pp. 93-96)

 ➢ Find the volume of a cuboid given its length, width, and height.

 A cuboid is a rectangular prism, or box shape.

In *Primary Mathematics 3B*, students learned to find the area of a rectangle given its length and width. Here, they will learn to find the volume of a rectangular solid given the length, width, and height.

Use multilink cubes or unit cubes. Form a single layer rectangle and ask your student for the volume. For example, make a rectangle with the cubes that is 4 by 3. The volume is 4 x 3 = 12 cubic units.
Point out that the height is 1 unit.
Add another layer and ask for the volume. Since we know how much is in one layer, we can find the number in both layers by multiplying. The volume is 12 x 2 = 24 cubic units.
Add another layer and ask for the volume.
There are now 3 layers with 12 in each layer.
The volume is 12 x 3 = 36 cubic units.
Continue until there are 5 layers. The final volume is 60 cubic units.
The length is 4 units, the width 3 units, and the height 5 units. We can find the volume by multiplying these measurements together.

Write

4 x 3 = 12

4 x 3 x 1 = 12

4 x 3 x 2 = 24
4 x 3 x 3 = 36
4 x 3 x 4 = 48
4 x 3 x 5 = 60
Volume
= length x width x height
= 4 units x 3 units x 5 units
= 60 cubic units

Point out that the order in which we multiply the sides does not matter. In the above example, it might be easier to mentally calculate the volume if we multiply the length by the height first.

4 x 3 x 5 = 4 x 5 x 3 = 20 x 3 = 60

Make a box. Use the **centimeter graph paper** to trace a box that is 13 cm by 8 cm. Trace a dotted line 2 cm in on all sides, and a solid line as shown below. Cut along the solid lines and fold along the dotted lines, overlapping the end, to get an open box.

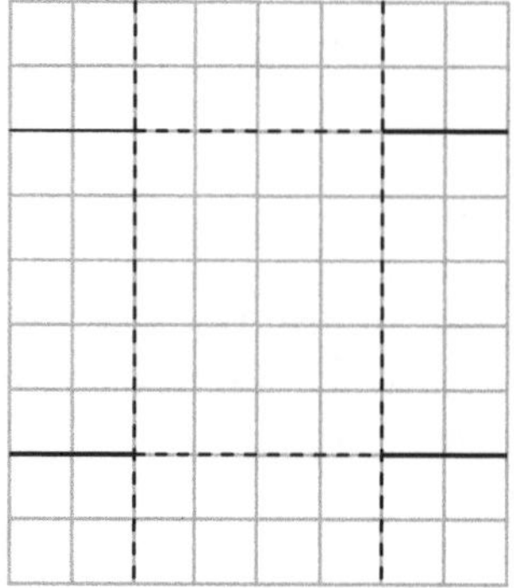

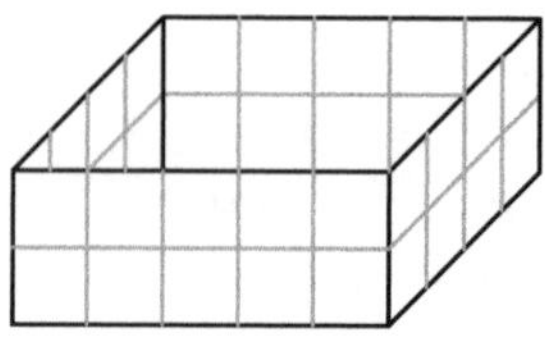

Have your student measure the sides of the box and multiply length x width x height, and then count the number of unit cubes that will fit inside. The volume is the same using both methods.

Page 93
Learning Tasks 1-6, pp. 94-96

24 cm^3

1. (a) 3; 2; 2; 12 (b) 5; 3; 1; 15
   (c) 3; 3; 3; 27 (d) 4; 2; 5; 40
2. 80
3. 2
4. 60
5. 27
6. A. 54 cm^3 B. 30,000 cm^3
   C. 350 m^3 D. 180 m^3

If you made a cubic foot in the last section, use it now. If you don't have one or want to make one, draw a cube and label each side 1 ft. Ask your student for the volume in cubic inches.

$1 \text{ ft}^3 = 12 \text{ in.} \times 12 \text{ in.} \times 12 \text{ in.} = 1{,}728 \text{ in.}^3$

Ask your student for the volume of a cubic yard in cubic feet.

$1 \text{ yd}^3 = 3 \text{ ft} \times 3 \text{ ft} \times 3 \text{ ft} = 27 \text{ ft}^3$

Workbook Exercise 50

(2) Liter (p. 97)

➢ Recognize the equivalency of 1 ml with 1 cm^3, and 1 ℓ with 1000 cm^3.

Show your student a **1-cm cube**, such as the unit cube of a **base-10 set**. Tell her that a box with a capacity the same size as the cube would hold 1 ml.

Draw a box and label it in centimeters. Ask for the volume in cubic centimeters and in milliliters.

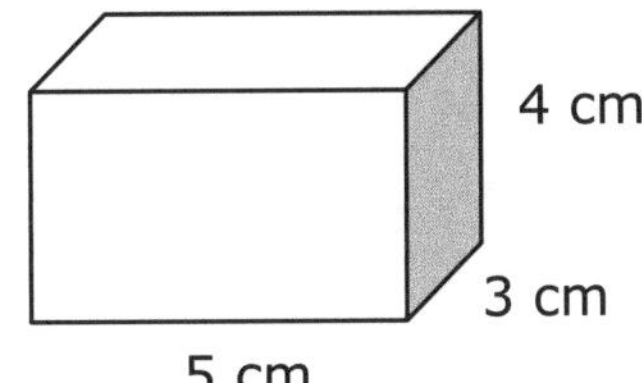

Volume = 5 cm x 3 cm x 4 cm = 60 cm^3 = 60 ml

Show your student the **thousand-block** from the base-10 set. Ask her for the volume. Tell her that this volume is the same as 1 liter.

1 ℓ = 1000 ml

Draw and label another box such that the volume will be greater than 1000 cm^3.

Ask your student for the volume in cubic centimeters, in milliliters, and in liters and milliliters.

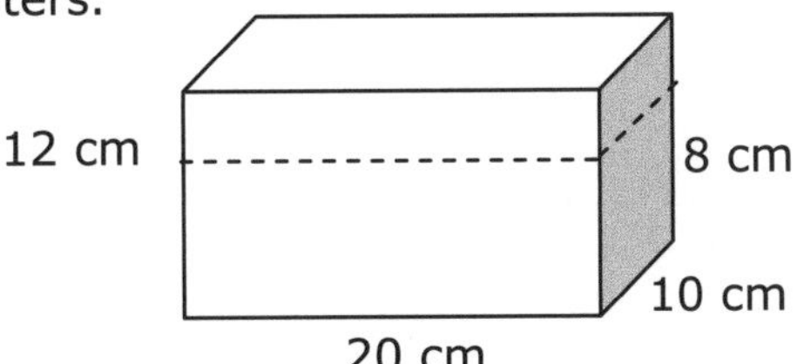

Volume = 20 cm x 10 cm x 12 cm = 2400 cm^3 = 2400 ml = 2 ℓ 400 ml

Ask, if this were a tank that was filled with water up to 8 cm height, what would be the volume of water?

Volume of water = 20 cm x 10 cm x 8 cm = 1600 ml = 1 ℓ 600 ml

How much more water would be needed to fill the tank?

2 ℓ 400 ml - 1 ℓ 600 ml = 800 ml

or 20 cm x 10 ml x 4 ml = 800 ml

Learning Tasks 7-10, p. 97

7. 1000; 1000; 1
8. (a) 2000 cm^3 (b) 400 cm^3 (c) 1200 cm^3
9. (a) 1 ℓ 750 ml (b) 2 ℓ 450 ml (c) 3 ℓ 50 ml
10. (a) 12,000 cm^3
    (b) 4800 cm^3; 4 ℓ 800 ml

Workbook Exercise 51

(3) Practice (pp. 98-99)

➢ Practice problems that involve volume.

Practice 6A, p. 98

US› 1. (a) 9 in.^{3} (b) 15 in.^{3}
3d› 1. (a) 9 cm^3 (b) 15 cm^3

2. Volume = 30 cm x 25 cm x 15 cm = **11,250 cm^3**

3. Volume = 5 cm x 5 cm x 5 cm = **125 cm^3**

US› 4. Capacity = 12 ft x 10 ft x 3 ft = **360 ft^3**
3d› 4. Capacity = 12 m x 10 m x 3 m = **360 m^3**

5. 8 x 5 x 3 = **120**

6. 30 cm x 20 cm x 20 cm = **12,000 cm^3**

Practice 6B, p. 99

1. (a) 3000 cm^3 (b) 250 cm^3 (c) 2060 cm^3

2. (a) 1 ℓ 50 ml (b) 1 ℓ 800 ml (c) 3 ℓ 500 ml

3. 15 cm x 10 cm x 3 cm = 450 cm^3 = **450 ml**

4. (a) Volume of water = 18 cm x 20 cm x 8 cm = **2880 cm^3**
   (b) 2880 cm^3 = 2880 ml = **2 ℓ 880 ml**

5. (a) 25 cm x 30 cm x 20 cm = **15,000 cm^3**
   (b) 15 cm x 10 cm x 20 cm = **3000 cm^3**

Review

Review E, pp. 100-104

1. (a) 79,431; 79,433; 80,331; 80,431
   (b) 0.09, 0.55, 0.6, 0.7
   (c) $2\frac{2}{9}$, $2\frac{4}{9}$, $2\frac{2}{3}$, $\frac{9}{2}$
2. (a) $1\frac{1}{4}$ (b) $1\frac{2}{9}$ (c) $4\frac{7}{10}$
   (d) $\frac{1}{6}$ (e) 8 (f) $13\frac{1}{3}$
3. Length of flower bed = 25 m - 14 m = 11 m
   Width of flower bed = 20 m - 14 m = 6 m
   Area = 11 m x 6 m = **66 m^2**
4. Amount used = $\frac{3}{5}$ x 600 g = **360 g**
5. 6 x 2 x 3 = **36**
6. (a) 2 units = $18
   1 unit = $18 ÷ 2 = $9
   3 units = $9 x 3 = $27
   Total money = **$27**

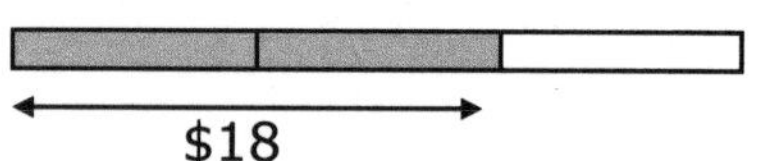

   (b) $\frac{1}{4}$ x 32 = **8**
7. (a) 1.6 (b) $2\frac{1}{20}$
8. (a) 24,000; 22,548
   (b) 42,000; 38,412
   (c) 15,000;14,455
9. A has 16 cubes, B has 12 cubes, so **4** have been removed.
10. (a) 6 (b) 2
11.

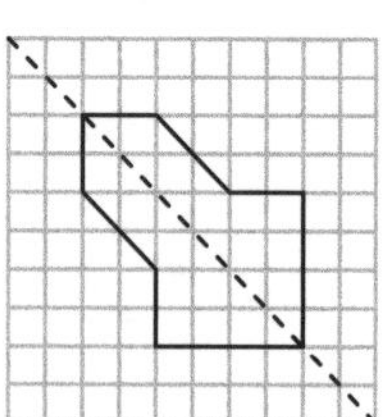

12. 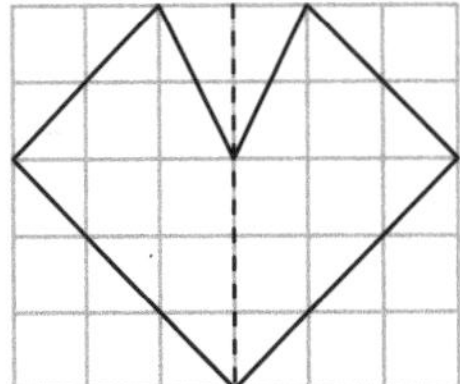

13. 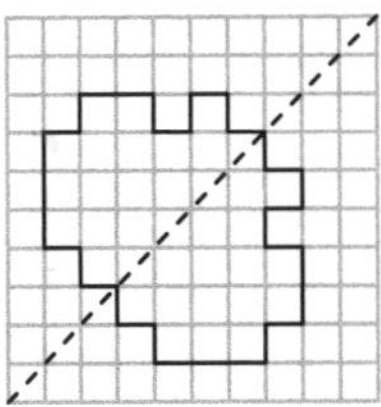

14. C

15. (a) Perimeter = 110 cm, Area = 460 cm^2
    (b) Perimeter = 60 m, Area = 128 m^2

16. (a) Area outside rectangle = 21 m x 11 m = 231 m^2
    Area inside rectangle = 15 m x 5 m = 75 m^2
    Area shaded part = 231 m^2 – 75 m^2 = **156 m^2**

    (b) Area large rectangle = 13 m x 11 m = 143 m^2
    Area small rectangle = 5 m x 7 m = 35 m^2
    Area shaded part = 143 m^2 – 35 m^2 = **108 m^2**

17. Length = 78 m^2 ÷ 6 m = 13 m
    Perimeter = 13 + 6 + 13 + 6 = **38 m**

18. Side = 48 cm ÷ 4 = **12 cm**
    Area = 12 cm x 12 cm = **144 cm^2**

19. Lace for each pillow case = 4.5 m ÷ 5 = **0.9 m or 90 cm**

20. Amount saved in 1 week = $70.50 ÷ 5 = $14.10
    Amount saved in 8 weeks = $14.10 x 8 = **$112.80**

21. 2 units = 200 – 40 = 160
    1 unit = 160 ÷ 2 = 80
    80 tickets were sold on Monday.

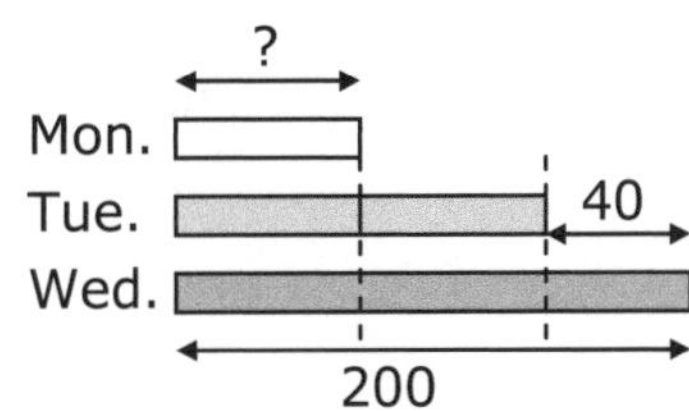

22. (a) $8 (b) March
    (c) Total savings = $8 + $14 + $17 + $14 + $11 = **$64**

Workbook Review 6
Workbook Review 7

Blank Page

Workbook Answers and Solutions

Exercise 1

1. (a) 0.2 (b) 0.5 (c) 0.8 (d) 0.9
2. (a) 0.4 (b) 0.7
3. (a) 0.9 (b) 0.5
4. (a) 0.2 (b) 0.6 (c) 0.9
5. (a) 0.8 (b) 0.4 (c) 0.5 (d) 0.1

Exercise 2

1. 6.3
2. (a) 6.4 (b) 9.7 (c) 8.2
3. (a) 1.6 (b) 2.4
4. (a) 2.8 (b) 1.4

Exercise 3

1. 0.3, 0.4, 0.5, $\frac{2}{10}$, $\frac{6}{10}$
   1.3, 1.4, 3.5, $1\frac{2}{10}$, $2\frac{2}{10}$
2. (a) 0.4 (b) 1.4 (c) 0.5 (d) 3.5
3. (a) $\frac{3}{10}$ (b) $2\frac{3}{10}$ (c) $\frac{3}{5}$ (d) $3\frac{3}{5}$
4. (a) 0.4, 1.3, 2.8
   (b) 8.8, 10.2,11.7
   (c) 59.5, 61.6, 64.4

US› 5. (a) $>$ (b) $>$ (c) $=$ (d) $>$

3d› 5. (a) is greater than (b) is greater than
(c) is equal to (d) is greater than

6. (a) 0.1 (b) 0.9
7. (a) 6.2 (b) 2.9
8. (a) 2.7, 2.9 (b) 6, 6.5

Exercise 4

1. (a) 34.6 (b) 50.7 (c) 45.3 (d) 40.9
2. (a) 0.8 (b) 0.3 (c) 90
   (d) 30 (e) 5 (f) 9
3. $1.2 = 1\frac{2}{10}$ $1\frac{5}{10} = 1.5$ $0.5 = \frac{5}{10}$ $\frac{9}{10} = 0.9$
   $4.1 = 4\frac{1}{10}$ $2\frac{8}{10} = 2.8$ $3\frac{7}{10} = 3.7$ $\frac{4}{10} = 0.4$
   $1\frac{3}{10} = 1.3$ $\frac{6}{10} = 0.6$ $1.4 = 1\frac{4}{10}$

Exercise 5

1. (a) 0.82 (b) 8.34 (c) 3.05 (d) 5.17 (e) 20.09
2. (a) 34.02 (b) 40.25 (c) 24.13 (d) 30.04
3. (a) 0, 0 (b) 0, 0 (c) tenths, $\frac{4}{10}$
   (d) tens, 50 (e) hundredths, 0.03 (f) ones, 0
4. (a) 0.03, 0.2, 0, 90 (b) 0.01, 0.4, 7, 80
   (c) 0.09, 0, 6, 50 (d) 0.8, 8, 10, 200

Exercise 6

1. (a) 0.07 (b) 1.07
   (c) 0.58 (d) 2.58
   (e) 0.24 (f) 1.24
   (g) 0.65 (h) 3.65
   (i) 0.03 (j) 2.03
   (k) 0.05 (l) 10.05
2. $\frac{9}{10} = 0.9$ $\frac{7}{100} = 0.07$ $\frac{17}{100} = 0.17$ $\frac{29}{100} = 0.29$
   $\frac{3}{10} = 0.3$ $\frac{9}{100} = 0.09$ $\frac{7}{10} = 0.7$

Exercise 7

1. (a) 80.7 (b) 24.5
   (c) 34.04 (d) 7.29
2. (a) $\frac{7}{100}$ (b) $\frac{5}{100}$ (c) $\frac{2}{10}$ (d) $\frac{7}{10}$ (e) $\frac{4}{10}$
3. (a) 0.04 (b) 0.05 (c) 0.1 (d) 0.08 (e) 0.3

4. (a) 1.0, 1.2 (b) 3, 3.5 (c) 2.7, 2.5
(d) 8.5, 7.5 (e) 0.2, 0.3 (f) 0.3, 0.25
(g) 0.08, 0.12 (h) 9.85, 9.75
5. (a) 0.13, 0.28 (b) 0.87, 0.97 (c) 3.08, 3.22, 3.37

Exercise 8

1. (a) $\frac{1}{2}$ (b) $2\frac{1}{2}$
(c) $\frac{2}{25}$ (d) $1\frac{2}{25}$
(e) $\frac{3}{20}$ (f) $3\frac{3}{20}$
(g) $\frac{16}{25}$ (h) $1\frac{16}{25}$
2. 2, 0.2
3. 75, 0.75
4. (a) 5, 0.5 (b) 5, 3.5
(c) $\frac{6}{10}$, 0.6 (d) $1\frac{6}{10}$, 1.6
(e) $\frac{25}{100}$, 0.25 (f) $2\frac{25}{100}$, 2.25
(g) $\frac{16}{100}$, 0.16 (h) $1\frac{16}{100}$, 1.16
5. (a) 0.8 (b) 3.8 (c) 0.45
(d) 1.45 (e) 0.06 (f) 2.06

Exercise 9

US› 1. (a) > (b) > (c) < (d) >
3d› 1. (a) greater than (b) greater than (c) less than (d) greater than

US› 2. (a) < (b) > (c) < (d) >
(e) = (f) > (g) = (h) >
3d› 2. (a) less than (b) greater than (c) less than (d) greater than
(e) equal to (f) greater than (g) equal to (h) greater than

3. (a) 0.88 (b) 0.61 (c) 2.99 (d) 0.42
4. (a) 3 (b) 8.1 (c) 5.33 (d) 7.01

Exercise 10

1. (a) 324.57 (b) 234.05

2. (a) 46.15 (b) 39.21 (c) 59.98 (d) 42.49
(e) 0.1 (f) 0.01 (g) 0.1 (h) 0.01

3. (a) 5.56 (b) 4.95
(c) 4.02 (d) 7.23
(e) 4.58 (f) 8.1
(g) 6.5 (h) 5.34

4. (a) 2.33 (b) 4.68
(c) 3.98 (d) 1.64
(e) 3.45 (f) 4.22
(g) 5.19 (h) 3.63

5. (b) 0.38 (c) 0.99 (d) 0.92

Exercise 11

1. (a) 0.004 (b) 4.007 (c) 0.083 (d) 0.435

2. (a) 0.003 (b) 0.406

3. (a) $\frac{9}{1000}$ (b) $\frac{43}{1000}$

4. (a) 3, 4, 7, 9 (b) 4, $\frac{4}{10}$ (c) $\frac{9}{1000}$ (d) $\frac{7}{100}$

5. (a) 8.4, 8.8, 9.1, 9.5
(b) 3.22, 3.25, 3.29, 3.32
(c) 5.999, 6.002, 6.007, 6.012
(d) 5.265, 5.269, 5.272, 5.275

Exercise 12

1. (a) 4.7 (b) 9.1
(c) 1.924 (d) 5

2. (a) 624.8 (b) 5.73 (c) 1.1

US› 3. (a) > (b) < (c) =
(d) > (e) > (f) <

3d› 3. (a) greater than (b) less than (c) equal to
(d) greater than (e) greater than (f) less than

4. 2.128, 2.18, 2.218, 2.8

5. 6.952, 6.3, 6.295, 6.03

Exercise 13

1. (a) $\mathbf{\frac{16}{25}}$ (b) $0.38 = \frac{38}{100} = \mathbf{\frac{19}{50}}$
   (c) $2.08 = 2\frac{8}{100} = \mathbf{2\frac{2}{25}}$ (d) $4.95 = 4\frac{95}{100} = \mathbf{4\frac{19}{20}}$
   (e) $0.216 = \frac{216}{1000} = \mathbf{\frac{27}{125}}$ (f) $0.352 = \frac{352}{1000} = \mathbf{\frac{44}{125}}$
   (g) $3.704 = 3\frac{704}{1000} = \mathbf{3\frac{88}{125}}$ (h) $2.425 = 2\frac{425}{1000} = \mathbf{2\frac{17}{40}}$
2. (a) 2.75 (b) 0.5 (c) $1\frac{1}{2}$ (d) 0.65
3. (a) 1.245, 1.254, 1.425, 1.524
   (b) 0.097, 0.119, 0.19, 0.91
   (c) $1\frac{9}{10}$, 2.5, $3\frac{1}{5}$, 3.95
   (d) 7.1, $7\frac{1}{5}$, 7.5, $7\frac{3}{5}$

Exercise 14

1. (a) 74 (b) 10 (c) 19 (d) 33
2. (a) 47 (b) 3 (c) 1 (d) 29
3. (a) \$3 (b) \$11
4. (a) 2 liters (b) 2 liters
5. (a) 40 (b) 46 (c) 6
   (d) 6 (e) 102 (f) 300

Exercise 15

1. (a) 4.7 (b) 8.1
2. (a) 1.5 liters (b) 20.3 kg (c) 9.1 m
3. 34.9 kg, 41.7 kg, 39.8 kg

Review 1

1. 92,405
2. thousands
3. 46,495
4. (a) 6000 (b) 42,096 (c) 90,800 (d) 27,481

5. 78,502
6. 0.03
7. 24,519
8. 30, 60
9. $\frac{8}{12}$
10. $\frac{7}{12}$
11. 13
12. 3.4
13. A-1.21 B-1.28 C-1.32
14. 4.5, 5
15. 2 km, 20 m, 253 cm, 2 m 35 cm
16. (a) $12 (b) Sumin

US› 17. Length of raffia left = 3 yd - $\frac{5}{6}$ yd = $\mathbf{2\frac{1}{6}}$ **yd**

3d› 17. Length of raffia left = 3 m - $\frac{5}{6}$ m = $\mathbf{2\frac{1}{6}}$ **m**

18. 30
19. Total length used = 15 m x $\frac{2}{3}$ = **10 m**
20. 127°
21. ∠d
22. ∠y = 90° – 37° = **53°**
23. $\frac{2}{7}$ x $35 = $10 Amount left = $35 – 10 = **$25**.
24. 3 units = 1650
1 unit = 1650 ÷ 3 = 550
2 units = 550 x 2 = 1100
There were **1100** boys.

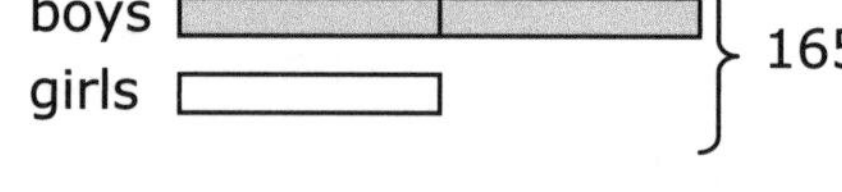

25. Amount paid in installments = 8 x $95 = $760
Total paid = $160 + $760 = **$920**

26. 2 longer units are girls.
Half of 1 unit wear spectacles
Total half units = 6
6 half units = 36
1 half unit = 36 ÷ 6 = 6

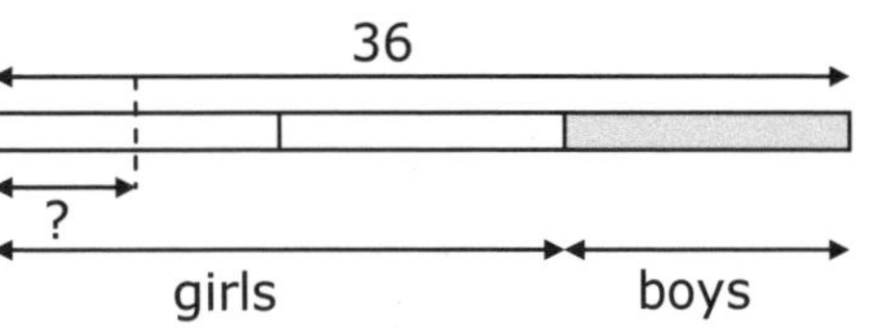

Or: Number of girls = $\frac{2}{3}$ x 36 = 24 $\frac{1}{4}$ x 24 = 6

6 girls wear glasses.

27. Length + side = 13 cm + 19 cm = 32 cm
Perimeter of rectangle = 32 cm x 2 = 64 cm = perimeter of square
Side of square = 64 cm ÷ 4 = **16 cm**

Review 2

1. 98,510
2. 1; 10; 100; 1,000; 10,000
3. $\frac{6}{10}$ or 0.6
4. 9
5. (a) 48,230 (b) 70.54
6. $4
7. $\frac{1100}{2000} = \mathbf{\frac{11}{20}}$
8. (a) 5.25 (b) 16.8
9. (a) $0.85 = \frac{85}{100} = \mathbf{\frac{17}{20}}$ (b) $2.4 = 2\frac{4}{10} = \mathbf{2\frac{2}{5}}$
10. 5
11. 495
12. 6.3
13. $35
13. (a) 6.05 (b) 3.7 (c) 0.61 (d) 6.7

US› 15. (a) > (b) =
3d› 15. (a) greater than (b) equal to

16. 10:15 a.m.
17. 4 km 360 m – 1 km 250 m = **3 km 110 m**
18. Total cookies = 98 + 42 = 140 $\frac{42}{140} = \frac{3}{10}$

$\mathbf{\frac{3}{10}}$ of the cookies were chocolate.

19. $\frac{2}{5}$

US› 20. Weight of other bag = 2 lb - $\frac{1}{4}$ lb = **$1\frac{3}{4}$ lb**

3d› 20. Weight of other bag = 2 kg - $\frac{1}{4}$ kg = **$1\frac{3}{4}$ kg**

21. Cost of book = $\frac{3}{8}$ x \$24 = **\$9**

22. Perimeter of garden = 2 x (35 m + 24 m) = 2 x 59 m = 118 m
Cost of fencing = 118 x \$10 = **\$1180**

US› 23. Width = 35 yd^2 ÷ 7 yd = **5 yd**
3d› 23. Width = 35 m^2 ÷ 7 m = **5 m**

24. 134°

25. (a) CD // IJ (b) GH ⊥ PQ

US› 26. Width = 1 unit
Perimeter = 6 units
6 units = 48 in.
1 unit = 48 in. ÷ 6 = 8 in.
2 units = 8 in. x 2 = 16 in.
or: 2 units = $\frac{1}{3}$ x 48 in. = 16 in.
The length of the rectangle is **16 in.**

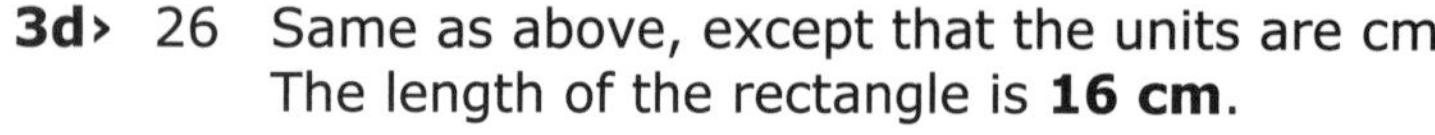

3d› 26 Same as above, except that the units are cm.
The length of the rectangle is **16 cm**.

27. 1 unit = boys
6 units = 84
1 unit = 84 ÷ 6 = 14
or: $\frac{1}{6}$ of 84 = 14
There are **14** boys.

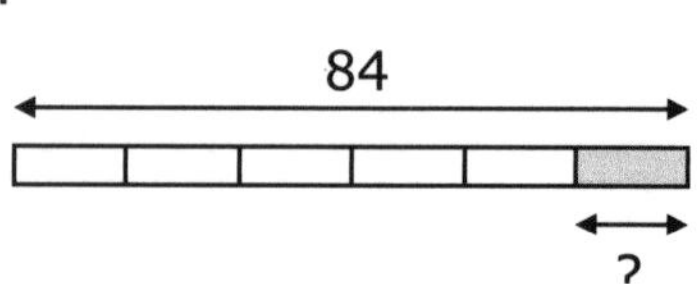

Review 3

1. P - 89,100 Q - 89,800 R - 90,400
2. (a) 6000 (b) 50,012 (c) 53,045
3. hundred
4. \$15,020
5. \$22.50
6. 0.02 or $\frac{2}{100}$
7. 5

8. (a) 21 (b) 48.02 (c) 0.06 (d) 0.2

9. 10.03

10. 40.26, 40.62, 42.06, 42.6

11. 490

12. 8 out of 16 squares are shaded. $\mathbf{\frac{1}{2}}$ of the figure is shaded.

13. $1\frac{3}{5}$

14. Cost of toy = $\frac{1}{9}$ x \$36 = **\$4**

15. Total juice = 250 ml x 6 = 1500 ml = 1 ℓ 500 ml

16. (a) 4,650 ml (b) 2,634 m
(c) 5,107 g (d) 184 min
(e) 4 h 20 min (f) 4 kg 7 g
(g) 5 m 80 cm (h) 3 ℓ 20 ml
US› (i) 6 lb 12 oz

US› 17. (a) 8 x 8 = 64 Length of one side = **8 in.**
(b) Perimeter = 8 in. x 4 = **32 in.**

3d› 17. (a) 8 x 8 = 64 Length of one side = **8 cm**
(b) Perimeter = 8 cm x 4 = **32 cm**

18. Figure can be divided up into two rectangles.
6 cm x 6 cm = 36 cm^2
4 cm x 9 cm = 36 cm^2
Total area = 36 cm^2 + 36 cm^2 = **72 cm^2**

19. 2

20. $\angle x = 150°$, $\angle y = 120°$

21.

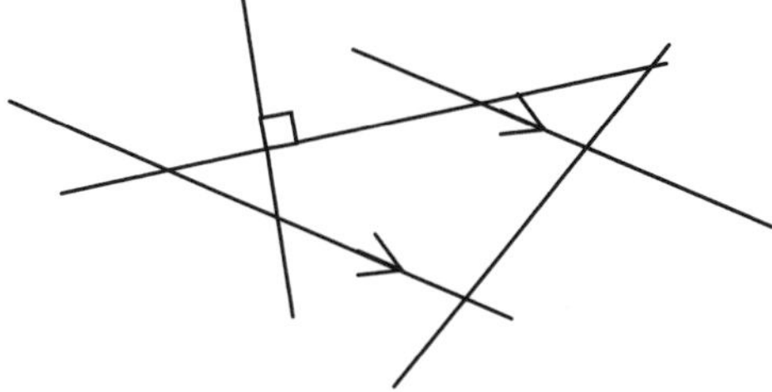

22. Weight of papaya = 1 kg 680 g – 800 g = 880 g
Total weight = 880 g + 1 kg 680 g = **2 kg 560 g**

23. Side of square = 20 cm ÷ 4 = 5 cm = width of rectangle
2 x width of rectangle = 5 cm x 2 = 10 cm
2 x length of rectangle = 36 cm + 10 cm = 26 cm
length of rectangle = 26 cm ÷ 2 = **13 cm**

24. Length cut off = $4 \times \frac{1}{5}$ m = $\frac{4}{5}$ m

Length remaining = 6 m - $\frac{4}{5}$ m = $\mathbf{5\frac{1}{5}}$ **m**

Exercise 16

1. (a) 0.8 (b) 1.2 (c) 0.6 (d) 1 (e) 1.4
2. (a) 0.06 (b) 0.12 (c) 0.05 (d) 0.1 (e) 0.11

Exercise 17

1. (a) 3.1 (b) 5.4 (c) 10.5 (d) 6.2
2. (a) 5 (b) 8.3 (c) 13.7 (d) 16.3

Exercise 18

1. (a) 2.73 (b) 2.55 (c) 5.05 (d) 4.57
   (e) 6.24 (f) 3.88 (g) 2.7 (h) 4.34
2. (a) 0.92 (b) 3.03 (c) 2.36 (d) 28.28
   (e) 3.62 (f) 9.61 (g) 17.34 (h) 68.18

Exercise 19

1. D 42.9 S 20.51 Q 44.09 M 90
   O 11.36 N 66.9 M 33.6 U 63
   I 27.35 J 88.75 A 68.05 V 82
   VANDA MISS JOAQUIM

Exercise 20

1. (a) 0.6 (b) 0.9 (c) 0.3 (d) 3.9
2. (a) 5.3 (b) 2.6 (c) 3.16 (d) 2.2

Exercise 21

1. (a) 0.05 (b) 0.65 (c) 0.85 (d) 0.92
2. (a) 4.38 (b) 1.48
3. (a) 0.42 (b) 3.24 (c) 2.78 (d) 6.06
   (e) 2.62 (f) 4.23 (g) 5.04 (h) 3.91

Exercise 22

1. (a) 2.1 (b) 2.7 (c) 3.6 (d) 1.6
   (e) 2.2 (f) 1.4 (g) 4.1 (h) 3.6

Exercise 23

1. (a) 2.44 (b) 2.55 (c) 0.07 (d) 8.78
   (e) 3.24 (f) 4.76 (g) 6.15 (h) 5.43

Exercise 24

1. T 2.35 E 3.08 H 0.43 U 4.65
   R 4.67 P 0.78 C 7.24 S 1.37
   I 7.38 G 4.16 O 8.96 N 6.78
   PENGUIN OSTRICH

Exercise 25

1. (a) 7.24, 7.23, 7.23
   (b) 11.63, 11.58, 11.58
   (c) 1.82, 1.83, 1.83
   (d) 4.05, 4.07, 4.07
2. (a) 9.79 (b) 10.64
3. (a) 4.26 (b) 4.58

Exercise 26

US› 1. Length used = 5 yd – 2.35 yd = **2.65 yd**
3d› 1. Length used = 5 m – 2.35 m = **2.65 m**

2. Weight gained = 5 kg – 3.6 kg = **1.4 kg**
3. Amount spent = \$36.45 - \$2.54 - **\$33.91**

Exercise 27

1. Total spent
   = \$1.40 + \$2.50 = \$3.90
   Amount left
   = \$13.50 - \$3.90 = **\$9.60**

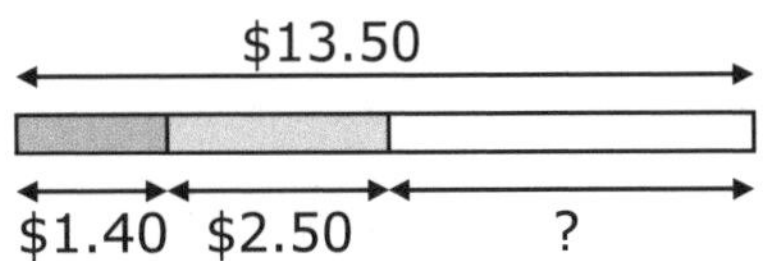

2. Total spent = \$12 + \$4.50 = \$16.50
   Change = \$20 - \$16.50 = **\$3.50**

3. Cost of kettle
   = \$38.90 + \$6.50 = \$45.40
   Total cost
   = \$45.40 + \$38.90 = **\$84.30**

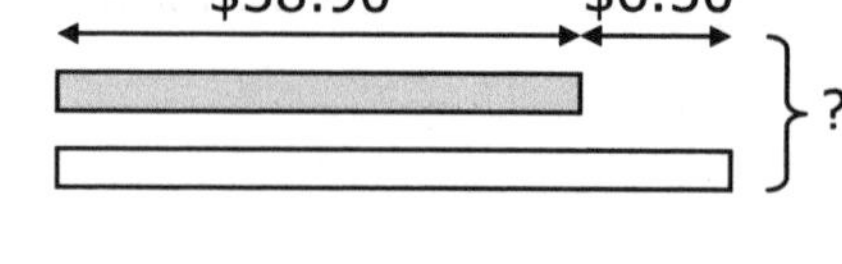

4. 1.63 – 0.38 – 0.25 = 1

US> Length of B = **1 ft**
3d> Length of B = **1 m**

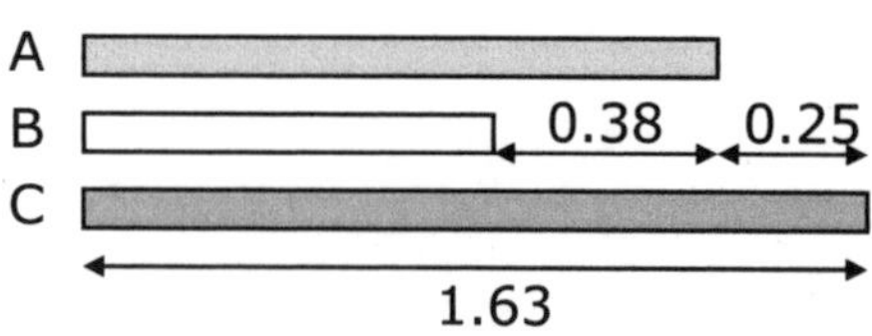

Exercise 28

1. (a) 0.8 (b) 1.8 (c) 1.4 (d) 3.6
   (e) 3.0 (f) 5.6 (g) 2.7 (h) 4.0

2. (a) 0.06 (b) 0.28 (c) 0.18 (d) 0.35
   (e) 0.3 (f) 0.72 (g) 0.12 (h) 0.48

Exercise 29

1. (a) 8.6 (b) 19.2
   (c) 16.8 (d) 42.3
   (e) 27.6 (f) 38.5
   (g) 132.5 (h) 244.8

Exercise 30

1. (a) 1.66 (b) 0.72
   (c) 15.78 (d) 27
   (e) 42.18 (f) 45.12
   (g) 579.46 (h) 582.48

Exercise 31

1. L 0.96 H 81.2 E 0.21 Y 14.73
   T 32.25 E 561 P 726.3 E 64.44
   N 36.45 D 3265.6 H 28.94 E 78.48
   HELP THE NEEDY

Exercise 32

US› 1. Total length = 1.25 yd x 3 = **3.75 yd**
3d› 1. Total length = 1.25 m x 3 = **3.75 m**

2. Capacity of fish tank = 5.7 ℓ x 5 = **28.5 ℓ**

3. Total saved = $2.50 x 6 = **$15**

Exercise 33

1.

1 can of chocolates =	$6.90
2 rolls of biscuits = $1.45 x 2 =	$2.90
Total	$9.80
2 bags of nuts = $3.75 x 2 =	$7.50
2 bottles of sauce = $0.95 x 2 =	$1.90
Total	$9.40
1 bath towel =	$9.95
4 face towels = $1.20 x 4 =	$4.80
Total	$14.75
3 dolls = $8 x 3 =	$24
1 teddy bear	$16.50
Total	$40.50

2. Amount of material used for pillow cases = 0.85 m x 2 = 1.7 m
Material remaining = 5 m – 1.7 m = **3.3 m**

3. Total spent = $1.35 x 6 = $8.10
Money she had at first = $2.50 + $8.10 = **$10.60**

Exercise 34

1. (a) 0.4 (b) 0.3 (c) 0.3 (d) 0.4
(e) 0.4 (f) 0.6 (g) $0.70 (h) $0.60
2. (a) 0.06 (b) 0.05 (c) 0.04 (d) 0.06
(e) 0.06 (f) 0.06 (g) $0.09 (h) $0.05

Exercise 35

1. (a) 0.24 (b) 0.21
(c) 0.13 (d) 0.19
(e) 0.28 (f) 0.17
(g) 0.13 (h) 0.12

2. (a) $0.95 (b) $0.85 (c) $0.35 (d) $0.90

Exercise 36

1. (a) 4.13 (b) 3.22
   (c) 1.47 (d) 2.68
   (e) 22.75 (f) 5.27
   (g) 20.14 (h) 7.05

2. (a) $1.05 (b) $1.15
   (c) $1.45 (d) $1.35
   (e) $1.15 (f) $1.09
   (g) $2.55 (h) $1.75

Exercise 37

1. (a) 1.4 (b) 0.75
   (c) 0.25 (d) 0.95
   (e) 1.24 (f) 1.25
   (g) 8.25 (h) 5.85
2. (a) 4.85 (b) 15.15
   (c) 11.75 (d) 9.72
   (e) 37.5 (f) 3.25
   (g) 0.25 (h) 29.35

Exercise 38

1. 4.6 20.3 7.6 6.0
   5.5 3.2 9.3 2.2
   9

Exercise 39

1. Length of each piece = 1.48 m ÷ 4 = **0.37 m**

2. Cost of 1 kg = $20.40 ÷ 3 = **$6.80**

US› 3. Amount Holly spent = $28.25 ÷ 5 = **$5.65**
3d› 3. Amount Devi spent = $28.25 ÷ 5 = **$5.65**

Exercise 40

1. Total spent = $3.15 + $4.65 = $7.80
   Amount each girl paid = $7.80 ÷ 2 = **$3.90**

2. Cost of 5 kg grapes = $50 - $18.75 = $31.25
   Cost of 1 kg of grapes = $31.25 ÷ 5 = **$6.25**

US› 3. Weight of 5 pieces of butter = 2.7 lb – 1.2 lb = 1.5 lb
Weight of 1 piece of butter = 1.5 lb ÷ 5 = **0.3 lb**

3d› 3. Weight of 5 pieces of butter = 2.7 kg – 1.2 kg = 1.5kg
Weight of 1 piece of butter = 1.5 kg ÷ 5 = **0.3 kg**

4. Total paint = 10.5 ℓ + 15.5 ℓ = 26 ℓ
Amount of paint in each can = 26 ℓ ÷ 4 = **6.5 ℓ**

Exercise 41

1. (a) 2 ℓ 450 ml x 2 **= 4 ℓ 900 ml**

(b) 2 m 65 cm x 3 = 6 m 195 cm = **7 m 95 cm**

(c) 6 km 250 m x 5 = 30 km + 1250 m = **31 km 250 m**

(d) 3 kg 300 g ÷ 3 = 3 kg ÷ 3 + 300 g ÷ 3 = **1 kg 100 g**

(e)
```
       1 h  50 min
   3 ) 5 h  30 min
       3
       2
           150 min
           150
```

(f) 1 600 ml ÷ 4 = 1600 ml ÷ 4 = **400 ml**

US› (g) 4 lb 3 oz x 6 = 24 lb + 18 oz = **25 lb 2 oz**

US› (h) 2 ft 10 in. x 4 = 8 ft 40 in. = **11 ft 4 in.**

2. Total capacity = 1 ℓ 500 ml x 3 = 3 ℓ 1500 ml = **4 ℓ 500 ml**

3. Total weight = 5 kg 500 g x 6 = 30 kg 3000 g = **33 kg**

4. Total time = 1 h 40 min x 4 = 4 h 160 min = **6 h 40 min**

5. Weight of each packet = 6 kg 750 g ÷ 9 = 6750 kg ÷ 9 = **750 g**

6. (a) 4 m ÷ 3 = 1 m remainder 1 m
1 m + 50 cm = 150 cm; 150 cm ÷ 3 = 50 cm
Each piece was **1 m 50 cm** long.
(b) Length used = 1 m 50 cm x 2 = 2 m 100 cm = **3 m**

7. Weight of books alone = 6 kg 850 g – 600 g = 6 kg 250 g
```
     1 kg  250 g
  5 )6 kg  250 g
     5
     1
          1250 g
          10
           250
           250
```
Weight of 1 book = **1 kg 250 g**

Review 4

1. (a) 10,590; 10,050; 9950; 9590; 9190
   (b) 8.3; 7.28; 2.83; 2.05
2. (a) 57.76 (b) 4.43 (c) 20.15 (d) 282
3. (a) 51.2 (b) 44
4. 26.08
5. A=5.78 B=5.84 C=5.87
6. 9 h 35 min
7. Height of brother = 1.7 m – 0.46 m = **1.24 m**
8. Total number of cookies = 48 x 10 = **480**
9. Amount left $= \frac{6}{8} = \mathbf{\frac{3}{4}}$
10. $\frac{8}{24} = \frac{1}{3}$ He sleeps $\mathbf{\frac{1}{3}}$ of a day.

US› 11. Amount needed = 4 gal - $\frac{3}{5}$ gal = $\mathbf{3\frac{2}{5}}$ **gal**

3d› 11. Amount needed = 4 ℓ - $\frac{3}{5}$ ℓ = $\mathbf{3\frac{2}{5}}$ **ℓ**

12. Number that cannot swim = $\frac{3}{8}$ x 40 = **15**
13. (a) 33º (b) 44º
14. Cost of 1 can peaches = \$1.20 x 2 = \$2.40
    Cost of 2 cans peaches = \$2.40 x 2 = \$4.80
    Total cost = \$1.20 x \$4.80 = **\$6.00**

US› 15. Total used = 1 ft 3 in. + 1 ft 8 in. = 2 ft 11 in.
Amount left = 6 ft – 2 ft 11 in. = **3 ft 1 in.**

3d› 15. Total used = 1 m 45 cm + 1 m 85 cm = 3 m 30 cm
Amount left = 6 m – 3 m 30 cm = **2 m 70 cm**

US› 16.

```
     1 lb  4 oz
6 ) 7 lb  8 oz
    6
    1
       24 oz
       24
       ==
```

Weight of 1 dictionary = **1 lb 4 oz**

3d› 16. 4 kg 200 g ÷ 6 = 4200 g ÷ 6 = 700g
Weight of 1 dictionary = **700 g**

Review 5

1. 80,000
2. 6
3. (a) 10,000 (b) 1000 (c) 5
4. (a) 4.54, 5.04, 20.5, 25.4
   (b) 3.515, 5.013, 10.513, 13.015
5. 12.65
6. 1400 km
7. (a) 0.5 (b) 3.72 (c) 0.5
8. 13
9. P: $3\frac{1}{4}$ Q: $3\frac{5}{8}$ R: $4\frac{1}{8}$
10. $\frac{2}{5}$
11. $1\frac{4}{5}, 1\frac{1}{8}, \frac{5}{6}, \frac{3}{4}$
12. $\frac{20}{100} = \frac{1}{5}$ 20 cm is $\mathbf{\frac{1}{5}}$ of a meter.
13. Total stamps = 98 + 98 + 153 = **349**
14. Total = 24 x 14 = **336**
15. Total = 25 x 4 x 12 = 100 x 12 = **1200**
16. Amount each paid = \$49.50 ÷ 3 = **\$16.50**
17. Total = 0.58 km x 6 = **3.48 km**
18. $\frac{12}{60} = \frac{1}{5}$ $\mathbf{\frac{1}{5}}$ of the workers are female.
19. 5 units = 10
    1 unit = 10 ÷ 5 = 2
    8 units = 16

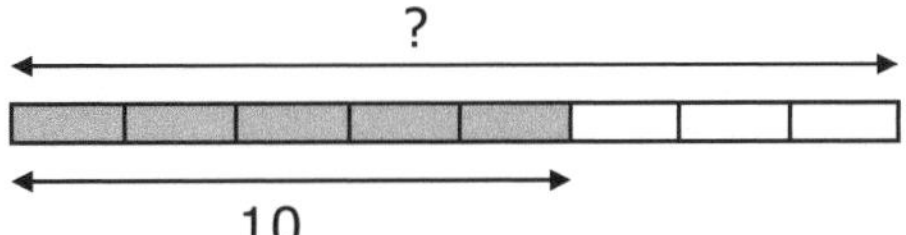

US› Capacity is **16 qt**
3d› Capacity is **16 ℓ**

20. 10.50 a.m.
21. 2 h 45 min
22. Cost of 20¢ stamps = 20¢ x 10 = \$2.00
    Cost of 35¢ stamps = 35¢ x 6 = \$2.10
    Cost of 50¢ stamps = 50¢ x 8 = \$4.00
    Total cost = \$2.00 + \$2.10 + \$4.00 = **\$8.10**

23. \$294

24. (a) Total = 6 + 9 + 16 + 12 = **43** (b) 4C

25. 5 units = \$2290
1 unit = \$2290 ÷ 5 = \$458
4 units = \$458 x 4 = \$1832
The computer costs **\$1832** more than the oven.

US› 26. Total weight of mushrooms = 0.43 lb x 6 = 2.58 lb
Weight of basket = 3.05 lb – 2.58 lb = **0.47 lb**

3d› 26. Total weight of mushrooms = 0.43 kg x 6 = 2.58 kg
Weight of basket = 3.05 kg – 2.58 kg = **0.47 kg**

Exercise 43

1. (a), (c), (d), (e), (g), and (h) are symmetrical.

2. (a) yes (b) no
(c) yes (d) yes
(e) no (f) no
(g) no (h) yes

Exercise 46

1. A 3 B 4 C 2
D 6 E 5 F 8

2. A 16 B 27 C 6 D 9 E 7

Exercise 47

1. (a) 1 (b) 2 (c) 2
2. (a) 1 (b) 2 (c) 2

Exercise 48

1. A 12 B 6 C 16
D 15 E 10 F 15
C has the greatest volume.
B has the smallest volume.

Exercise 49

1. (a) 6 (b) 6
(c) 18 (d) 16
(e) 6 (f) 9

Exercise 50

US› 1. (b) 2 in., 2 in., 2 in., 8 in.^{3}
(c) 5 in., 2 in., 4 in., 40 in.^{3}
(d) 3 in., 2 in., 7 in., 42 in.^{3}
(e) 7 in., 3 in., 2 in., 42 in.^{3}

3d› 1. (b) 2 cm, 2 cm, 2 cm, 8 cm^3
(c) 5 cm, 2 cm, 4 cm, 40 cm^3
(d) 3 cm, 2 cm, 7 cm, 42 cm^3
(e) 7 cm, 3 cm, 2 cm, 42 cm^3

2. 18 cm^3 200 cm^3 126 cm^3 192 cm^3 240 cm^3

Exercise 51

1. (a) 300 cm^3 (b) 800 cm^3
2. (a) 400 ml (b) 120 ml
3. (a) 4 liters (b) 3 liters
4. 1 ℓ 200 ml 3 ℓ 600 ml
   1 ℓ 200 ml 3 ℓ 600 ml
   2 ℓ 160 ml 1 ℓ 440 ml

Review 6

1. (a) 79,031 (b) 55,100 (c) 23.29 (d) 18.21
2. (a) 1 (b) 9
3. (a) $35,500 (b) 8 m **US›** (c) 17 yd
4. (a) $\frac{4}{6}$ (or $\frac{2}{3}$), 1
   (b) 3.15, 3.35
5. 3.05
6. 0.4
7. $\frac{5}{7}$
8. $2\frac{2}{5}$
9. (a) 6.66 (b) 0.27 (c) 24 (d) 0.55
10. **9** There are 3 thirds in 1, so there are 3 x 3 = 9 thirds in 3.
11. 4.3
12. Difference = 2 kg 450 g – 865 g = **1 kg 585 g**

13. 4 units = \$1800
 1 unit = \$1800 ÷ 4 = \$450
 Total = \$1800 + \$450 = \$2250
 or total = 5 units = \$450 x 5 = \$2250
 Total cost = **\$2250**

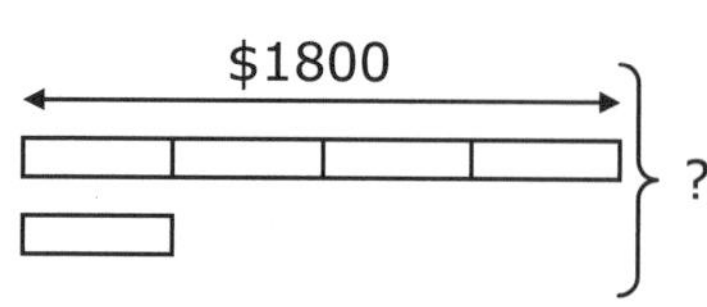

14. Cost of shirts = \$12.50 x 2 = \$25.00
 Total money = \$39.85 + \$25.00 = **\$64.85**

15. $\frac{32}{40} = \frac{4}{5}$ He answered $\mathbf{\frac{4}{5}}$ of the items correctly.

16. Cost of lunch = $\frac{1}{10}$ x \$20 = **\$2**

17. Check line.

18. Check angle.

19. Volume of solid P = 11 cm^3, volume of solid Q = 7 cm^3.
 Difference = **4 cm^3**

20. 1 unit = \$61.20 - \$14.80 = \$46.40
 2 units = \$46.40 x 2 = \$92.80
 He received **\$92.80**

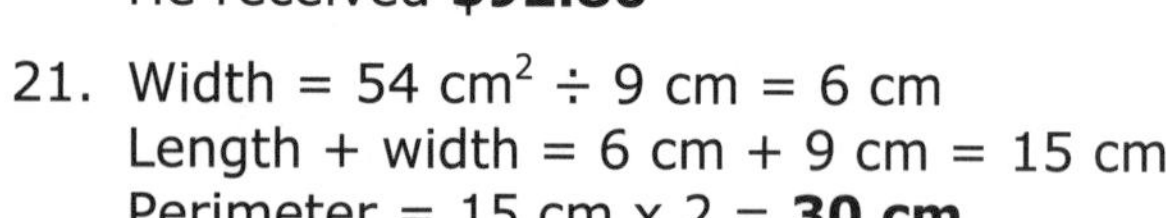

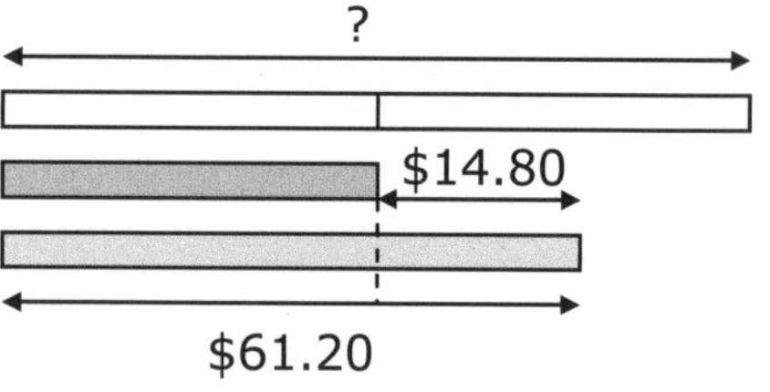

21. Width = 54 cm^2 ÷ 9 cm = 6 cm
 Length + width = 6 cm + 9 cm = 15 cm
 Perimeter = 15 cm x 2 = **30 cm**

US› 22. Amount left after making dress = 4.5 ft – 0.9 ft = 3.6 ft
 Amount for each cushion = 3.6 ft ÷ 5 = **0.72 ft**

3d› 22. Amount left after making dress = 4.5 m – 0.9 m = 3.6 m
 Amount for each cushion = 3.6 m ÷ 5 = **0.72 m**

23. 2 units = \$14
 1 unit = \$14 ÷ 2 = \$7
 3 units = \$7 x 3 = \$21
 The racket cost **\$21**.

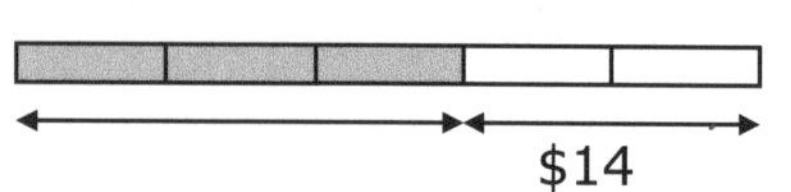

Review 7

1. (a) 1000 (b) 0.1
2. 40.6
3. 6.0
4. (a) 1, 2, 4, 5, 10, 20
 (b) 1, 2, 4
5. 13,600

US› 6. 147.3 lb

3d› 6. 147.3 kg

7. 4.32

8. $\frac{3}{8}$

9. 1.5

10. (a) 1 ℓ 540 ml (b) 3650

11. 1 ℓ 200 ml ÷ 3 = 1200 ml ÷ 3 = **400 ml**

12. Total length = 3.82 m x 6 = **22.92 m**

US› 13. 8 ft ÷ 6 = **1.3 ft**
3d› 13. 8 m ÷ 6 = **1.3 m**

US› 14. Cost of shrimp = $1.50 x 5 = $7.50
Total cost = $7.50 + $4.50 = **$12**
3d› 14. Cost of prawns = $1.50 x 5 = $7.50
Total cost = $7.50 + $4.50 = **$12**

15. Amount of money left = $1.50 - $0.50 = $1.00
Fraction left = $\frac{100}{150} = \mathbf{\frac{2}{3}}$

16. Amount spent on food = $\frac{2}{5}$ x $840 = **$336**

US› 17. Length + width = 45 yd + 20 yd = 65 yd
Perimeter = 65 yd x 2 = 130 yd
Distance he walked = 130 yd x 5 = **650 yd**
3d› 17. Length + width = 45 m + 20 m = 65 m
Perimeter = 65 m x 2 = 130 m
Distance he walked = 130 m x 5 = **650 m**

18. 2

19. 9 cm^3

20. Total water = 15 m x 6 m x 4 m = **360 m^3**

21. Width of card = 30 cm + 6 cm = 36 cm
Length of card = 24 cm + 6 cm = 30 cm
Length + width = 36 cm + 30 cm = 66 cm
Perimeter = 66 cm x 2 = **132 cm**

22. 3 units = $45
1 unit = $45 ÷ 3 = $15
He had $15 left.

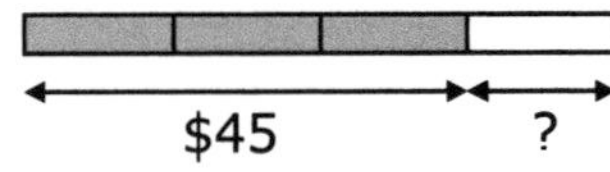

23. (a) Number of students wearing glasses = 6 + 14 + 10 + 4 = **34**

US› 24. Capacity of bucket = $\frac{1}{7}$ x 30.1 gal = **4.3 gal**

US› 25. Perimeter = 6 units

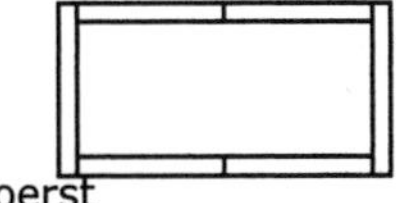

6 units = 30 in.
1 unit = 30 ÷ 6 = 5 in. = width
2 units = 5 in. x 2 = 10 in.
Area = 5 in. x 10 in. = **50 in.^{2}**

US› 26. 15 quarters = $0.25 x 15 = $3.75
35 nickels = $0.05 x 35 = $1.75
21 dimes = $0.10 x 21 = $2.10
Total money = $3.75 + $1.75 + $2.10 = **$7.60**

US› 27. There are 4 quarters in $1
Number of quarters in $116 = $116 x 4 = $464
Number of quarters in $0.75 = 3
Total number of quarters in $116.75 = **467**

Mental Math 1			
1.	0.5	14.	0.35
2.	0.05	15.	4.15
3.	0.2	16.	0.6
4.	0.04	17.	7.08
5.	0.25	18.	0.7
6.	0.02	19.	6.8
7.	0.1	20.	0.21
8.	0.06	21.	5.12
9.	3.16	22.	9.36
10.	0.75	23.	0.55
11.	0.28	24.	8.4
12.	10.8	25.	0.24
13.	0.32	26.	0.18

Mental Math 2			
1.	0.68	16.	0.8
2.	0.84	17.	6.28
3.	1.63	18.	4.41
4.	0.6	19.	1.71
5.	0.73	20.	8.34
6.	0.62	21.	3.08
7.	2.83	22.	3.3
8.	1.02	23.	5.2
9.	5.1	24.	10.7
10.	1.45	25.	6.98
11.	4.02	26.	6.51
12.	087	27.	2.12
13.	0.27	28.	1.49
14.	6.82	29.	1.31
15.	1.62	30.	10.89

Mental Math 3			
1.	0.75	16.	0.29
2.	0.25	17.	0.38
3.	0.01	18.	0.77
4.	0.96	19.	0.81
5.	0.48	20.	0.65
6.	0.35	21.	0.12
7.	0.67	22.	0.27
8.	0.35	23.	0.51
9.	0.58	24.	0.72
10.	0.38	25.	0.84
11.	0.45	26.	0.95
12.	0.09	27.	0.41
13.	0.16	28.	0.85
14.	0.55	29.	0.13
15.	0.93	30.	0.48

Mental Math 4			
1.	0.005	16.	1.206
2.	0.011	17.	3.898
3.	0.136	18.	0.149
4.	1.009	19.	1.448
5.	2.224	20.	4.03
6.	5.19	21.	8.105
7.	6.268	22.	6.591
8.	0.111	23.	1.872
9.	9.019	24.	3.372
10.	9.442	25.	7.059
11.	0.102	26.	9.004
12.	7.54	27.	2.606
13.	2.272	28.	4.011
14.	2.36	29.	0.991
15.	8.605	30.	6.234

Mental Math 5			
1.	6	16.	13
2.	9	17.	12.7
3.	9.5	18.	12.1
4.	8.5	19.	11.1
5.	12.3	20.	11.3
6.	10	21.	14.4
7.	8.1	22.	7.2
8.	9.2	23.	9.7
9.	12.2	24.	13.9
10.	10.8	25.	15.3
11.	5.9	26.	5.3
12.	4.2	27.	8.9
13.	11	28.	14.8
14.	11.2	29.	14.3
15.	14	30.	15.9

Mental Math 6			
1.	0.78	16.	1.31
2.	1.08	17.	0.85
3.	0.68	18.	0.51
4.	1.13	19.	5.38
5.	0.2	20.	3.97
6.	1.42	21.	3.9
7.	1	22.	5.79
8.	1.22	23.	2.46
9.	0.94	24.	2.07
10.	1.18	25.	2.6
11.	0.71	26.	5.32
12.	0.9	27.	1.15
13.	1.45	28.	5.12
14.	0.4	29.	3.4
15.	0.72	30.	9.64

Mental Math 7			
1.	4.4	16.	5.31
2.	9.3	17.	3.46
3.	3.4	18.	7.44
4.	2.6	19.	2.54
5.	1.9	20.	1.9
6.	7.2	21.	4.44
7.	6.7	22.	6.5
8.	4.6	23.	4.6
9.	3.5	24.	7.23
10.	6.3	25.	4.5
11.	5.6	26.	9.01
12.	7.9	27.	5.4
13.	8.8	28.	6.93
14.	8	29.	4.96
15.	7.5	30.	0.46

Mental Math 8			
1.	0.83	16.	0.62
2.	5.61	17.	0.24
3.	0.02	18.	0.67
4.	0.06	19.	2.51
5.	0.52	20.	4.25
6.	0.86	21.	5.16
7.	9.52	22.	7.57
8.	6.43	23.	2.15
9.	4.28	24.	0.52
10.	3.44	25.	3.92
11.	0.93	26.	0.15
12.	0.96	27.	0.94
13.	1.91	28.	0.86
14.	7.94	29.	1.54
15.	3.98	30.	4.34

Mental Math 9			
1.	0.95	16.	2.75
2.	1.8	17.	0.28
3.	4.64	18.	3.67
4.	3.48	19.	2.79
5.	2.23	20.	2.37
6.	4.57	21.	4.83
7.	3.48	22.	3.18
8.	2.54	23.	6.65
9.	2.34	24.	1.87
10.	4.46	25.	5.43
11.	2.56	26.	1.38
12.	6.83	27.	6.26
13.	1.17	28.	3.53
14.	4.79	29.	7.15
15.	2.26	30.	2.31

Mental Math 10			
1.	4.1	16.	1.5
2.	2.4	17.	3.4
3.	3.8	18.	3.9
4.	3.3	19.	3.2
5.	5.7	20.	1.8
6.	0.4	21.	3.5
7.	3.9	22.	3.8
8.	2.3	23.	2.6
9.	1.9	24.	4.5
10.	3.5	25.	2.8
11.	1.5	26.	0.7
12.	1.8	27.	2.4
13.	3.9	28.	4.8
14.	2.7	29.	2.7
15.	2.3	30.	5.4

Mental Math 11			
1.	4.23	16.	11.61
2.	5.63	17.	6.19
3.	8.03	18.	5.75
4.	7.32	19.	1.04
5.	6.63	20.	7.82
6.	7.26	21.	4.03
7.	13.11	22.	1.6
8.	7.08	23.	8.22
9.	7.43	24.	1.07
10.	6.28	25.	1.21
11.	4.56	26.	3.42
12.	5.23	27.	4.68
13.	0.88	28.	9.77
14.	2.51	29.	4.03
15.	4.11	30.	5.55

Mental Math 12			
1.	3.2	16.	1.5
2.	4.9	17.	4
3.	1.8	18.	0.42
4.	0.12	19.	0.81
5.	0.24	20.	2.8
6.	3.5	21.	1
7.	0.36	22.	4.5
8.	0.72	23.	2.1
9.	5.6	24.	0.64
10.	2.7	25.	0.3
11.	0.24	26.	0.63
12.	0.2	27.	4.8
13.	5.4	28.	0.25
14.	1.6	29.	1.4
15.	0.18	30.	0.36

Mental Math 13			
1.	23.1		
2.	15 + 2 = 17		
3.	48 + 1.8 = 49.8		
4.	16 + 1.2 = 17.2		
5.	24 + 3 = 27		
6.	42.5	16.	32
7.	43.4	17.	14.1
8.	16.5	18.	12.4
9.	12.9	19.	55.2
10.	50.4	20.	8.4
11.	4.6	21.	57.4
12.	16.8	22.	19.6
13.	25.2	23.	7.2
14.	14.2	24.	24.9
15.	8.4	25.	13.5

Mental Math 14			
1.	0.3	16.	0.8
2.	0.8	17.	0.7
3.	0.06	18.	0.3
4.	0.05	19.	0.08
5.	0.6	20.	0.3
6.	0.06	21.	0.09
7.	0.04	22.	0.03
8.	0.9	23.	0.09
9.	0.07	24.	0.4
10.	0.5	25.	0.4
11.	0.03	26.	0.8
12.	0.07	27.	0.6
13.	0.05	28.	0.07
14.	0.9	29.	0.8
15.	0.08	30.	0.3

Mental Math 15			
1.	6.66	16.	0.64
2.	0.3	17.	2.2
3.	1.164	18.	6.318
4.	10.3	19.	0.06
5.	6.28	20.	0.7
6.	0.09	21.	3.82
7.	0.04	22.	0.53
8.	5.32	23.	0.55
9.	9.1	24.	6.3
10.	4.96	25.	0.8
11.	0.32	26.	5.78
12.	6.65	27.	2.46
13.	5.55	28.	2.4
14.	2.53	29.	1.13
15.	3.24	30.	0.9

Blank page

Mental Math 1

Write as a decimal

1. $\frac{1}{2}$ =

2. $\frac{1}{20}$ =

3. $\frac{1}{5}$ =

4. $\frac{1}{25}$ =

5. $\frac{1}{4}$ =

6. $\frac{1}{50}$ =

7. $\frac{1}{10}$ =

8. $\frac{3}{50}$ =

9. $3\frac{4}{25}$ =

10. $\frac{3}{4}$ =

11. $\frac{7}{25}$ =

12. $10\frac{4}{5}$ =

13. $\frac{8}{25}$ =

14. $\frac{7}{20}$ =

15. $4\frac{3}{20}$

16. $\frac{3}{5}$ =

17. $7\frac{2}{25}$ =

18. $\frac{7}{10}$ =

19. $6\frac{4}{5}$ =

20. $\frac{21}{100}$ =

21. $5\frac{3}{25}$ =

22. $9\frac{9}{25}$ =

23. $\frac{11}{20}$

24. $8\frac{2}{5}$ =

25. $\frac{6}{25}$ =

26. $\frac{9}{50}$

Mental Math 2

1. 0.38 + 0.3 = ________
2. 0.89 − 0.05 = ________
3. 0.73 + 0.9 = ________
4. 0.52 + 0.08 = ________
5. 0.93 − 0.2 = ________
6. 0.66 − 0.04 = ________
7. 2.53 + 0.3 = ________
8. 1.62 − 0.6 = ________
9. 5.02 + 0.08 = ________
10. 0.55 + 0.9 = ________
11. 3.62 + 0.4 = ________
12. 0.92 − 0.05 = ________
13. 0.22 + 0.05 = ________
14. 6.88 − 0.06 = ________
15. 2.32 − 0.7 = ________
16. 1.6 − 0.8 = ________
17. 6.36 − 0.08 = ________
18. 4.4 + 0.01 = ________
19. 1.64 + 0.07 = ________
20. 8.4 − 0.06 = ________
21. 2.28 + 0.8 = ________
22. 3.7 − 0.4 = ________
23. 5.19 + 0.01 = ________
24. 9.9 + 0.8 = ________
25. 7.48 − 0.5 = ________
26. 6.44 + 0.07 = ________
27. 1.32 + 0.8 = ________
28. 1.52 − 0.03 = ________
29. 1.26 + 0.05 = ________
30. 9.99 + 0.9 = ________

Mental Math 3

1. 0.25 + ______ = 1
2. 0.75 + ______ = 1
3. 0.99 + ______ = 1
4. 0.04 + ______ = 1
5. 0.52 + ______ = 1
6. 0.65 + ______ = 1
7. 0.33 + ______ = 1
8. 0.65 + ______ = 1
9. 0.42 + ______ = 1
10. 0.62 + ______ = 1
11. 0.55 + ______ = 1
12. 0.91 + ______ = 1
13. 0.84 + ______ = 1
14. 0.45 + ______ = 1
15. 0.07 + ______ = 1
16. 0.71 + ______ = 1
17. 0.62 + ______ = 1
18. 0.23 + ______ = 1
19. 0.19 + ______ = 1
20. 0.35 + ______ = 1
21. 0.88 + ______ = 1
22. 0.73 + ______ = 1
23. 0.49 + ______ = 1
24. 0.28 + ______ = 1
25. 0.16 + ______ = 1
26. 0.05 + ______ = 1
27. 0.59 + ______ = 1
28. 0.15 + ______ = 1
29. 0.87 + ______ = 1
30. 0.52 + ______ = 1

Mental Math 4

1. 0.003 + 0.002 = ________
2. 0.014 - 0.003 = ________
3. 0.126 + 0.01 = ________
4. 0.209 + 0.8 = ________
5. 2.231 - 0.007 = ________
6. 5.198 - 0.008 = ________
7. 6.218 + 0.05 = ________
8. 0.171 - 0.06 = ________
9. 9.01 + 0.009 = ________
10. 8.842 + 0.6 = ________
11. 0.142 - 0.04 = ________
12. 7.543 - 0.003 = ________
13. 1.472 + 0.8 = ________
14. 2.355 + 0.005 = ________
15. 9.105 - 0.5 = ________
16. 1.506 - 0.3 = ________
17. 3.896 + 0.002 = ________
18. 0.119 + 0.03 = ________
19. 1.648 - 0.2 = ________
20. 4.028 + 0.002 = ________
21. 8.1 + 0.005 = ________
22. 6.991 - 0.4 = ________
23. 1.875 - 0.003 = ________
24. 4.172 - 0.8 = ________
25. 7.052 + 0.007 = ________
26. 9.204 - 0.2 = ________
27. 2.666 - 0.06 = ________
28. 3.311 + 0.7 = ________
29. 0.985 + 0.006 = ________
30. 6.324 - 0.09 = ________

Mental Math 5

1. 5.1 + 0.9 = ________
2. 8.8 + 0.2 = ________
3. 9.3 + 0.2 = ________
4. 7.9 + 0.6 = ________
5. 8.2 + 4.1 = ________
6. 4.3 + 5.7 = ________
7. 6.6 + 1.5 = ________
8. 6.6 + 2.6 = ________
9. 8 + 4.2 = ________
10. 9.5 + 1.3 = ________
11. 5.2 + 0.7 = ________
12. 0.8 + 3.4 = ________
13. 3.2 + 7.8 = ________
14. 6.7 + 4.5 = ________
15. 9.1 + 4.9 = ________
16. 9.5 + 3.5 = ________
17. 2.9 + 9.8 = ________
18. 5.9 + 6.2 = ________
19. 2.4 + 8.7 = ________
20. 3.6 + 7.7 = ________
21. 4.5 + 9.9 = ________
22. 2.8 + 4.4 = ________
23. 0.2 + 9.5 = ________
24. 4.2 + 9.7 = ________
25. 8.2 + 7.1 = ________
26. 4.8 + 0.5 = ________
27. 3.4 + 5.5 = ________
28. 6.8 + 8 = ________
29. 9.9 + 4.4 = ________
30. 7.7 + 8.2 = ________

Mental Math 6

1. $0.72 + 0.06 =$ _________
2. $0.48 + 0.6 =$ _________
3. $0.09 + 0.59 =$ _________
4. $0.63 + 0.5 =$ _________
5. $0.16 + 0.04 =$ _________
6. $0.62 + 0.8 =$ _________
7. $0.92 + 0.08 =$ _________
8. $0.42 + 0.8 =$ _________
9. $0.91 + 0.03 =$ _________
10. $0.58 + 0.6 =$ _________
11. $0.62 + 0.09 =$ _________
12. $0.86 + 0.04 =$ _________
13. $0.65 + 0.8 =$ _________
14. $0.34 + 0.06 =$ _________
15. $0.03 + 0.69 =$ _________
16. $0.41 + 0.9 =$ _________
17. $0.78 + 0.07 =$ _________
18. $0.49 + 0.02 =$ _________
19. $4.48 + 0.9 =$ _________
20. $3.27 + 0.7 =$ _________
21. $3.82 + 0.08 =$ _________
22. $5.69 + 0.1 =$ _________
23. $2.39 + 0.07 =$ _________
24. $1.67 + 0.4 =$ _________
25. $2.51 + 0.09 =$ _________
26. $4.82 + 0.5 =$ _________
27. $1.09 + 0.06 =$ _________
28. $4.82 + 0.3 =$ _________
29. $0.07 + 3.33 =$ _________
30. $0.9 + 8.74 =$ _________

Mental Math 7

1. 4.9 – 0.5 = ________
2. 9.6 – 0.3 = ________
3. 4.2 – 0.8 = ________
4. 3.3 – 0.7 = ________
5. 2.5 – 0.6 = ________
6. 8.1 – 0.9 = ________
7. 7.3 – 0.6 = ________
8. 5.4 – 0.8 = ________
9. 3.7 – 0.2 = ________
10. 6.5 – 0.2 = ________
11. 6.3 – 0.7 = ________
12. 8.2 – 0.3 = ________
13. 9.4 – 0.6 = ________
14. 8.5 – 0.5 = ________
15. 7.9 – 0.4 = ________
16. 6.21 – 0.9 = ________
17. 4.36 – 0.9 = ________
18. 8.04 – 0.6 = ________
19. 3.24 – 0.7 = ________
20. 2.3 – 0.4 = ________
21. 5.14 – 0.7 = ________
22. 7.2 – 0.7 = ________
23. 5.5 – 0.9 = ________
24. 7.73 – 0.5 = ________
25. 5.3 – 0.8 = ________
26. 9.41 – 0.4 = ________
27. 5.9 – 0.5 = ________
28. 7.43 – 0.5 = ________
29. 5.66 – 0.7 = ________
30. 1.36 – 0.9 = ________

Mental Math 8

1. 0.85 − 0.02 = ________
2. 5.69 − 0.08 = ________
3. 0.1 − 0.08 = ________
4. 0.1 − 0.04 = ________
5. 0.6 − 0.08 = ________
6. 0.9 − 0.04 = ________
7. 9.6 − 0.08 = ________
8. 6.5 − 0.07 = ________
9. 4.3 − 0.02 = ________
10. 3.5 − 0.06 = ________
11. 1 − 0.07 = ________
12. 1 − 0.04 = ________
13. 2 − 0.09 = ________
14. 8 − 0.06 = ________
15. 4 − 0.02 = ________
16. 1 − 0.38 = ________
17. 1 − 0.76 = ________
18. 1 − 0.33 = ________
19. 3 − 0.49 = ________
20. 5 − 0.75 = ________
21. 6 − 0.84 = ________
22. 8 − 0.43 = ________
23. 3 − 0.85 = ________
24. 0.58 − 0.06 = ________
25. 3.95 − 0.03 = ________
26. 0.2 − 0.05= ________
27. 1 − 0.06 = ________
28. 0.9 − 0.04 = ________
29. 2 − 0.46 = ________
30. 5 − 0.66 = ________

Mental Math 9

1. 0.98 – 0.03 = ________
2. 1.84 – 0.04 = ________
3. 4.73 – 0.09 = ________
4. 3.5 – 0.02 = ________
5. 2.3 – 0.07 = ________
6. 4.66 – 0.09 = ________
7. 3.53 – 0.05 = ________
8. 2.6 – 0.06 = ________
9. 2.42 – 0.08 = ________
10. 4.55 – 0.09 = ________
11. 2.6 – 0.04 = ________
12. 6.92 – 0.09 = ________
13. 1.22 – 0.05 = ________
14. 4.85 – 0.06 = ________
15. 2.32 – 0.06 = ________
16. 2.83 – 0.08 = ________
17. 0.36 – 0.08 = ________
18. 3.74 – 0.07 = ________
19. 2.87 – 0.08 = ________
20. 2.43 – 0.06 = ________
21. 4.9 – 0.07 = ________
22. 3.27 – 0.09 = ________
23. 6.72 – 0.07 = ________
24. 1.95 – 0.08 = ________
25. 5.48 – 0.05 = ________
26. 1.45 – 0.07 = ________
27. 6.34 – 0.08 = ________
28. 3.57 – 0.04 = ________
29. 7.2 – 0.05 = ________
30. 2.91 – 0.6 = ________

Mental Math 10

1. 6.9 - 2.8 = ________
2. 5.6 - 3.2 = ________
3. 5.6 - 1.8 = ________
4. 9.7 - 6.4 = ________
5. 9.5 - 3.8 = ________
6. 5.2 - 4.8 = ________
7. 8.4 - 4.5 = ________
8. 6 - 3.7 = ________
9. 4.1 - 2.2 = ________
10. 5.8 - 2.3 = ________
11. 8 - 6.5 = ________
12. 4.2 - 2.4 = ________
13. 6.4 - 2.5 = ________
14. 5.5 - 2.8 = ________
15. 8.4 - 6.1 = ________
16. 5.3 - 3.8 = ________
17. 7 - 3.6 = ________
18. 7.7 - 3.8 = ________
19. 8.1 - 4.9 = ________
20. 5.3 - 3.5 = ________
21. 6.7 - 3.2 = ________
22. 8.1 - 4.3 = ________
23. 6.8 - 3.2 = ________
24. 9.2 - 4.7 = ________
25. 8.7 - 5.9 = ________
26. 2.3 - 1.6= ________
27. 4 - 1.6 = ________
28. 9 - 4.2 = ________
29. 7.4 - 4.7 = ________
30. 10 - 4.6 = ________

Mental Math 11

1. 3.24 + 0.99= ________
2. 4.66 + 0.97 = ________
3. 7.05 + 0.98= ________
4. 6.37 + 0.95= ________
5. 5.67 + 0.96= ________
6. 4.28 + 2.98 = ________
7. 8.12 + 4.99 = ________
8. 2.99 + 4.09 = ________
9. 8.42 - 0.99 = ________
10. 7.25 - 0.97 = ________
11. 5.54 - 0.98 = ________
12. 7.22 - 1.99 = ________
13. 3.83 - 2.95 = ________
14. 7.47 - 4.96 = ________
15. 8.09 - 3.98 = ________
16. 6.66 + 4.95 = ________
17. 3.97 + 2.22 = ________
18. 8.71 - 2.96 = ________
19. 6.02 - 4.98 = ________
20. 3.87 + 3.95 = ________
21. 7.01 - 2.98 = ________
22. 5.57 - 3.97 = ________
23. 1.99 + 6.23 = ________
24. 4.03 - 2.96 = ________
25. 5.2 - 3.99 = ________
26. 6.4 - 2.98 = ________
27. 3.7 + 0.98 = ________
28. 4.8 + 4.97 = ________
29. 3.05 + 0.98 = ________
30. 6.5 - 0.95 = ________

Mental Math 12

1. 0.4 x 8 = ________
2. 0.7 x 7 = ________
3. 0.2 x 9 = ________
4. 0.06 x 2 = ________
5. 0.03 x 8 = ________
6. 7 x 0.5 = ________
7. 6 x 0.06 = ________
8. 0.09 x 8 = ________
9. 0.7 x 8 = ________
10. 0.3 x 9 = ________
11. 0.06 x 4 = ________
12. 4 x 0.05 = ________
13. 6 x 0.9 = ________
14. 0.8 x 2 = ________
15. 0.03 x 6 = ________
16. 0.5 x 3 = ________
17. 0.8 x 5 = ________
18. 0.06 x 7 = ________
19. 9 x 0.09 = ________
20. 0.4 x 7 = ________
21. 0.2 x 5 = ________
22. 9 x 0.5 = ________
23. 0.7 x 3 = ________
24. 0.08 x 8 = ________
25. 0.05 x 6 = ________
26. 9 x 0.07 = ________
27. 0.6 x 8 = ________
28. 0.05 x 5 = ________
29. 0.2 x 7 = ________
30. 0.04 x 9 = ________

Mental Math 13

1. 7.7 x 3 = 21 + 2.1 = ________

2. 3.4 x 5 = ______ + _______ = __________

3. 8.3 x 6 = ______ + _______ = __________

4. 4.3 x 4 = ______ + _______ = __________

5. 4.5 x 6 = ______ + _______ = __________

6. 8.5 x 5 = ________

7. 6.2 x 7 = ________

8. 3.3 x 5 = ________

9. 4.3 x 3 = ________

10. 6.3 x 8 = ________

11. 2.3 x 2 = ________

12. 5.6 x 3 = ________

13. 3.6 x 7 = ________

14. 7.1 x 2 = ________

15. 2.1 x 4 = ________

16. 6.4 x 5 = ________

17. 4.7 x 3 = ________

18. 3.1 x 4 = ________

19. 6.9 x 8 = ________

20. 2.8 x 3 = ________

21. 8.2 x 7 = ________

22. 4.9 x 4 = ________

23. 3.6 x 2 = ________

24. 8.3 x 3 = ________

25. 2.7 x 5 = ________

Mental Math 14

1. $1.5 \div 5 =$ _________
2. $6.4 \div 8 =$ _________
3. $0.42 \div 7 =$ _________
4. $0.3 \div 6 =$ _________
5. $5.4 \div 9 =$ _________
6. $0.24 \div 4 =$ _________
7. $0.2 \div 5 =$ _________
8. $8.1 \div 9 =$ _________
9. $0.49 \div 7 =$ _________
10. $4 \div 8 =$ _________
11. $0.27 \div 9 =$ _________
12. $0.21 \div 3 =$ _________
13. $0.25 \div 5 =$ _________
14. $4.5 \div 5 =$ _________
15. $0.16 \div 2 =$ _________
16. $3.2 \div 4 =$ _________
17. $3.5 \div 5 =$ _________
18. $2.4 \div 8 =$ _________
19. $0.48 \div 6 =$ _________
20. $1.8 \div 6 =$ _________
21. $0.63 \div 7 =$ _________
22. $0.12 \div 4 =$ _________
23. $0.18 \div 2 =$ _________
24. $3.6 \div 9 =$ _________
25. $1.6 \div 4 =$ _________
26. $7.2 \div 9 =$ _________
27. $3.6 \div 6 =$ _________
28. $0.14 \div 2 =$ _________
29. $5.6 \div 7 =$ _________
30. $0.9 \div 3 =$ _________

Mental Math 15

1. 6.26 + 0.4 = ________
2. 0.06 x 5 = ________
3. 0.174 – 0.01 = ________
4. 7.8 + 2.5 = = ________
5. 6.36 – 0.08 = ________
6. 0.63 ÷ 7 = ________
7. 0.1 - 0.06 = ________
8. 6.3 – 0.98 = ________
9. 9.4 – 0.3 = ________
10. 5 – 0.04 = ________
11. 0.04 x 8 = ________
12. 6.73 – 0.08 = ________
13. 4.56 + 0.99 = ________
14. 2.6 - 0.07 = ________
15. 7.21 - 3.97 = ________
16. 0.56 + .08 = ________
17. 2.6 – 0.4 = ________
18. 6.218 + 0.1 = ________
19. 0.3 ÷ 5 = ________
20. 1.5 – 0.8 = ________
21. 4.32 – 0.5 = ________
22. 0.6 – 0.07 = ________
23. 1 - 0.45 = ________
24. 9 x 0.7 = ________
25. 4 ÷ 5 = ________
26. 6 – 0.22 = ________
27. 3 – 0.54 = ________
28. 4 – 1.6 = ________
29. 1.63 – 0.5 = ________
30. 7.2 ÷ 8 = ________

Exercise 3.1

1. Multiply in compound units.

   (a) 4 ℓ 230 ml x 9 = __________ ℓ __________ ml

   (b) 12 m 62 cm x 8 = __________ m __________ cm

   (c) 3 ft 9 in. x 12 = __________ ft __________ in.

   (d) 4 gal 3 c x 7 = __________ gal __________ c

   (e) 8 min 15 s x 5 = __________ min __________ s

2. Give your answer to the following problems in compound units.

   (a) The side of a square picture frame measures 1 ft 4 in. What is its perimeter?

   (b) Mariellen bought 10 cans of soup. Each can weighed 1 lb 4 oz. What was the total weight?

   (c) A seamstress bought some cloth. She cut 4 pieces of cloth to make some shirts. Each piece was 2 yd 4 in. long. There was 1 yd 8 in. left over. What was the length of the cloth she bought?

   (d) One week Josh jogged for 1 h 25 min every day on Monday through Saturday, and for 40 minutes on Sunday. How much time did he spend jogging that week?

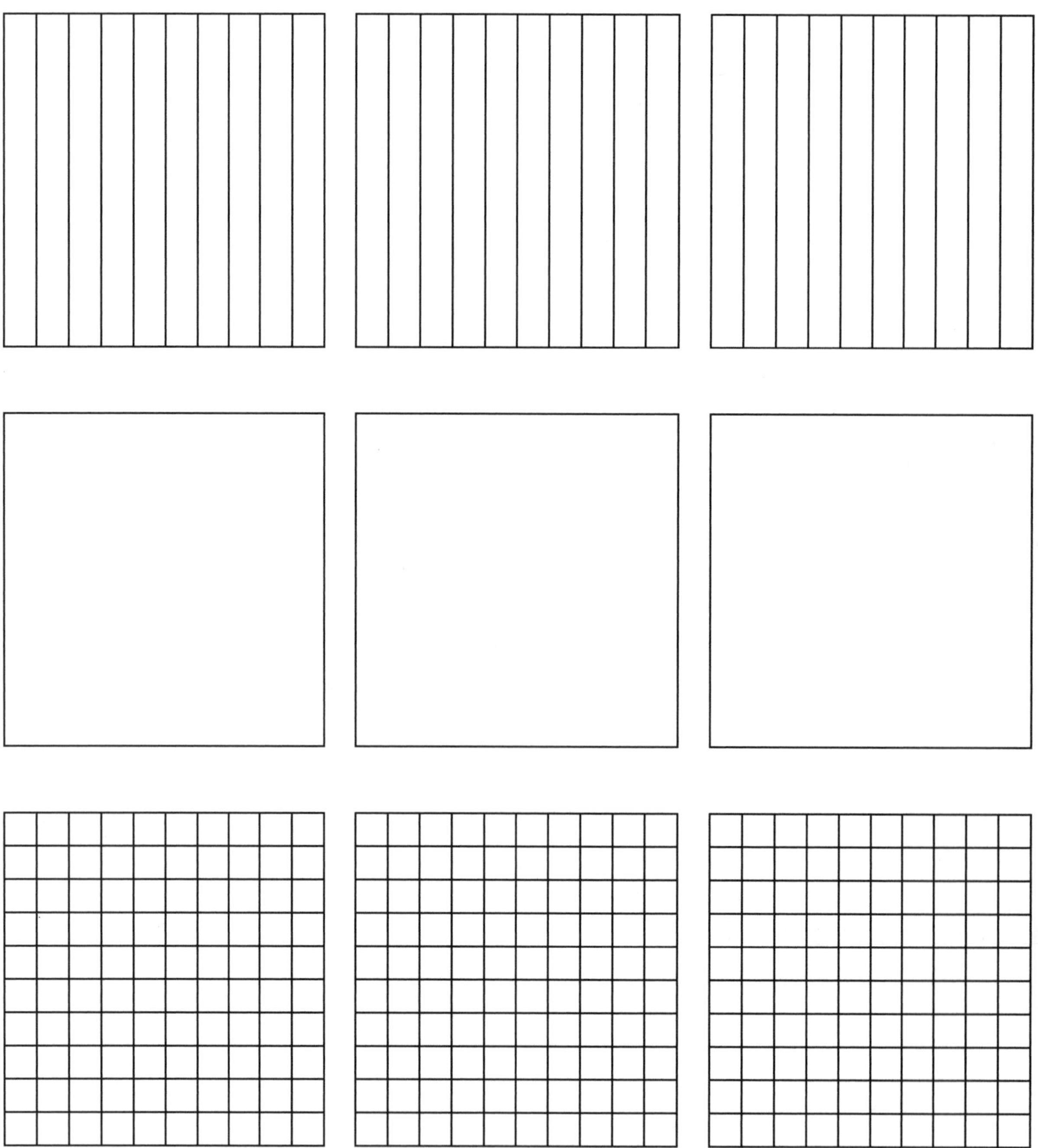

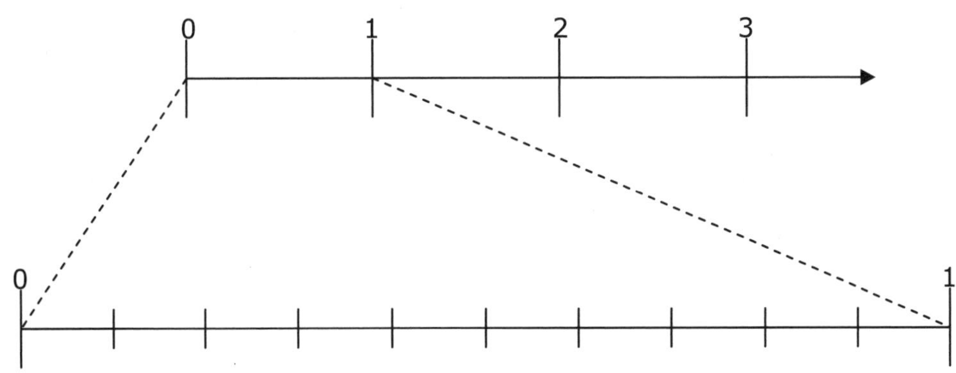
0
1
2
3
0
1

0
1
2
3
4
5

20
21
22
23
24
25

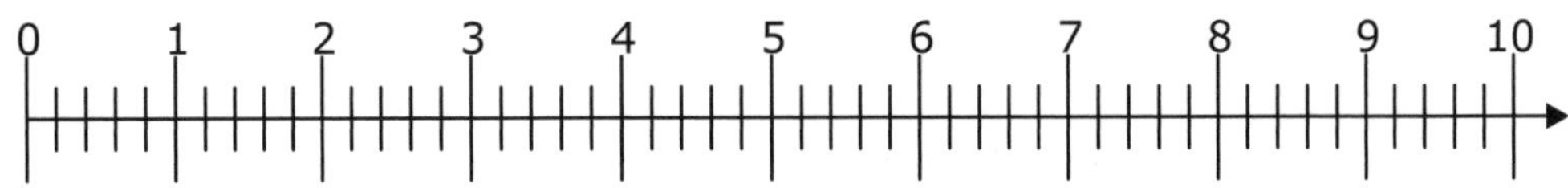
0
1
2
3
4
5
6
7
8
9
10

1	2	3	4	5	6	7	8	9	10
11	12	13	14	15	16	17	18	19	20
21	22	23	24	25	26	27	28	29	30
31	32	33	34	35	36	37	38	39	40
41	42	43	44	45	46	47	48	49	50
51	52	53	54	55	56	57	58	59	60
61	62	63	64	65	66	67	68	69	70
71	72	73	74	75	76	77	78	79	80
81	82	83	84	85	86	87	88	89	90
91	92	93	94	95	96	97	98	99	100

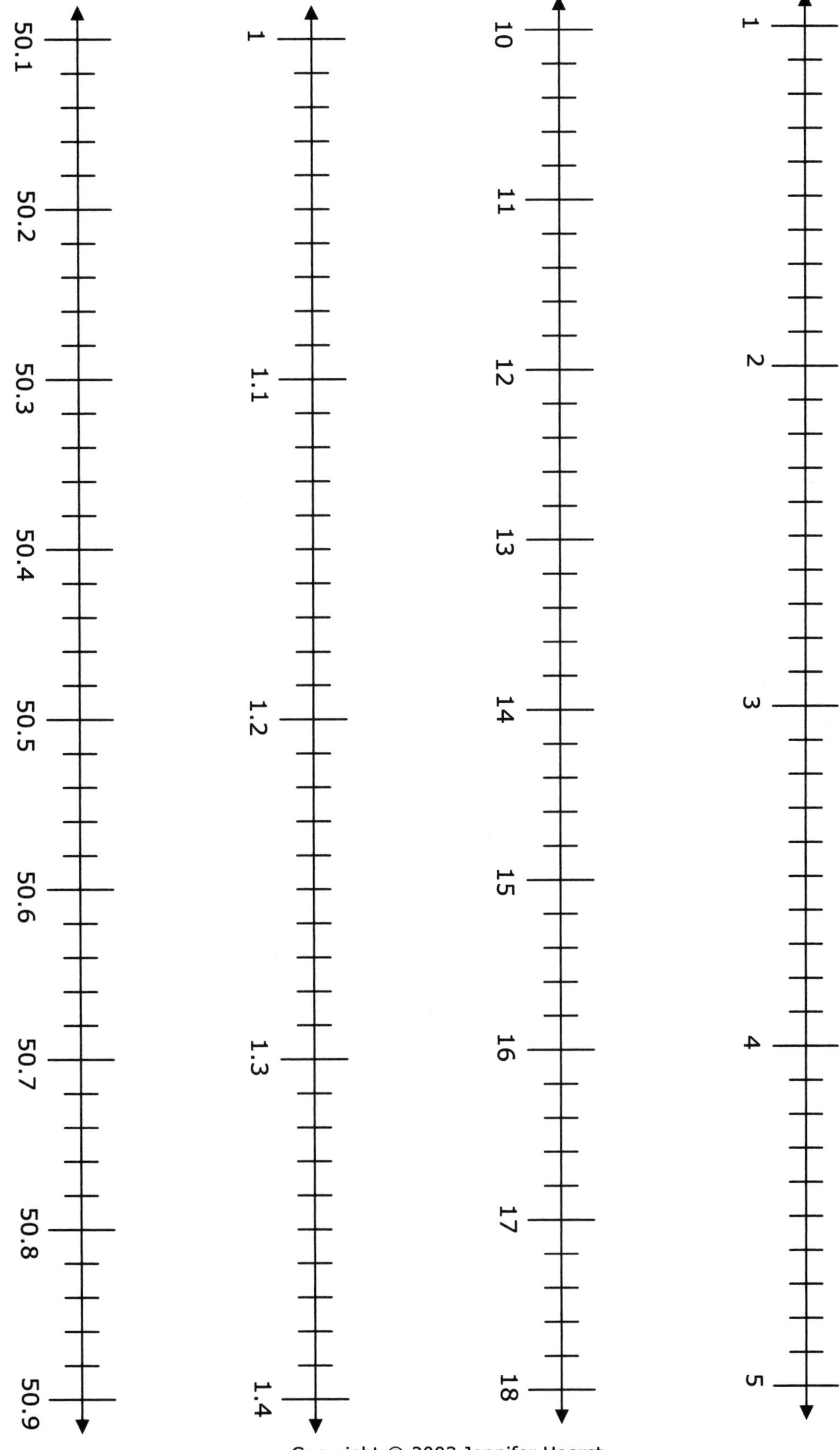
1
2
3
4
5
10
11
12
13
14
15
16
17
18
1
1.1
1.2
1.3
1.4
50.1
50.2
50.3
50.4
50.5
50.6
50.7
50.8
50.9

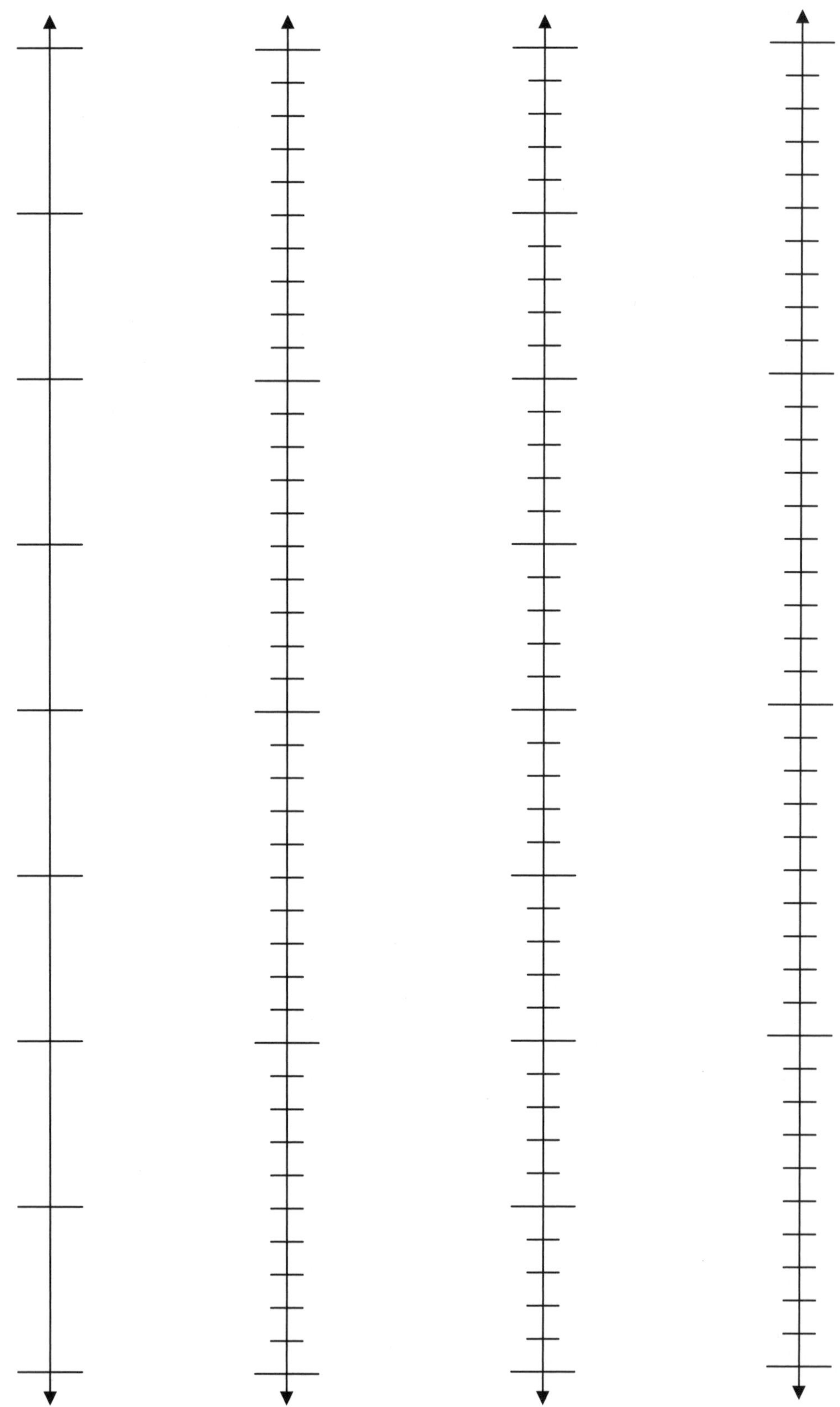

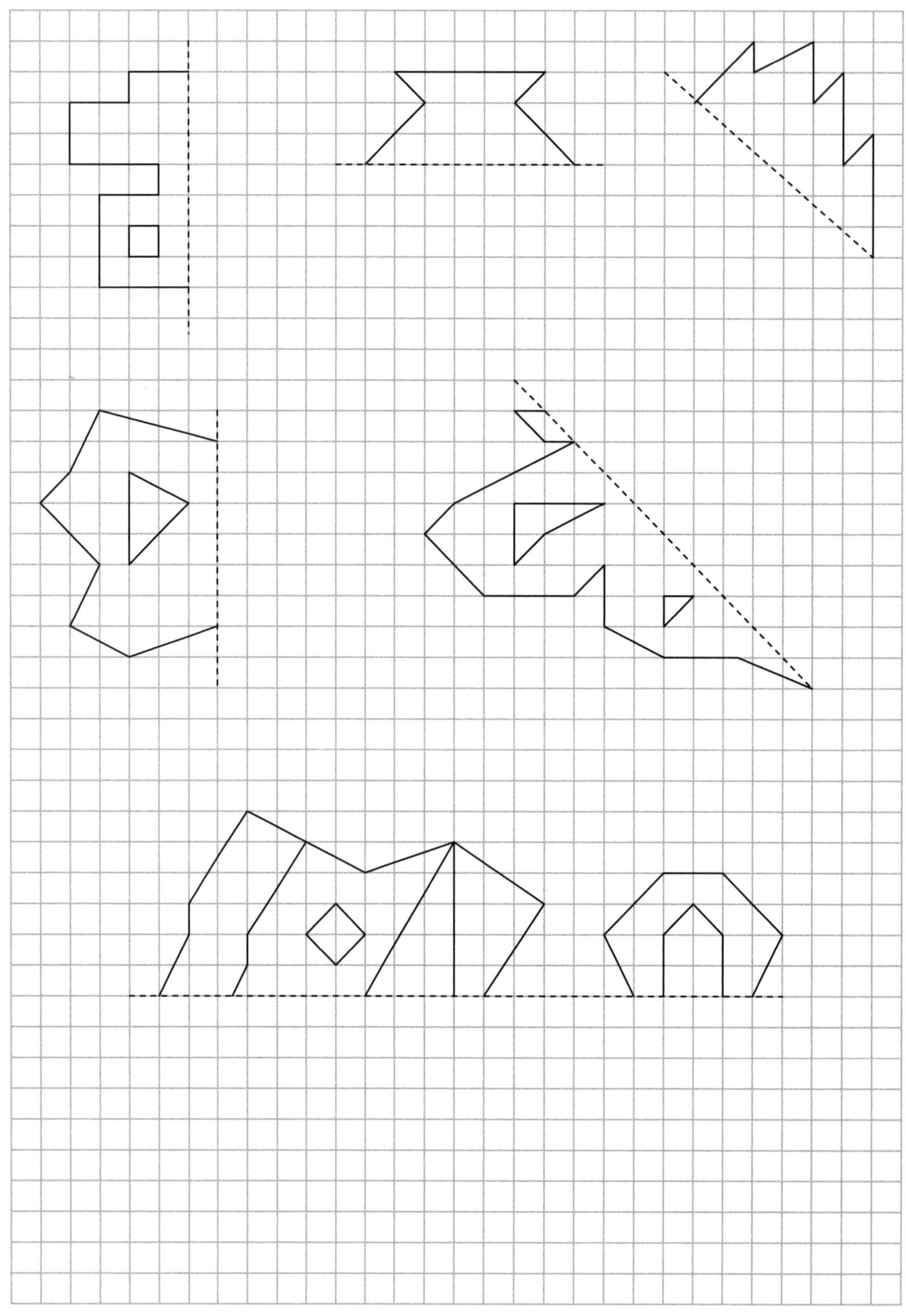

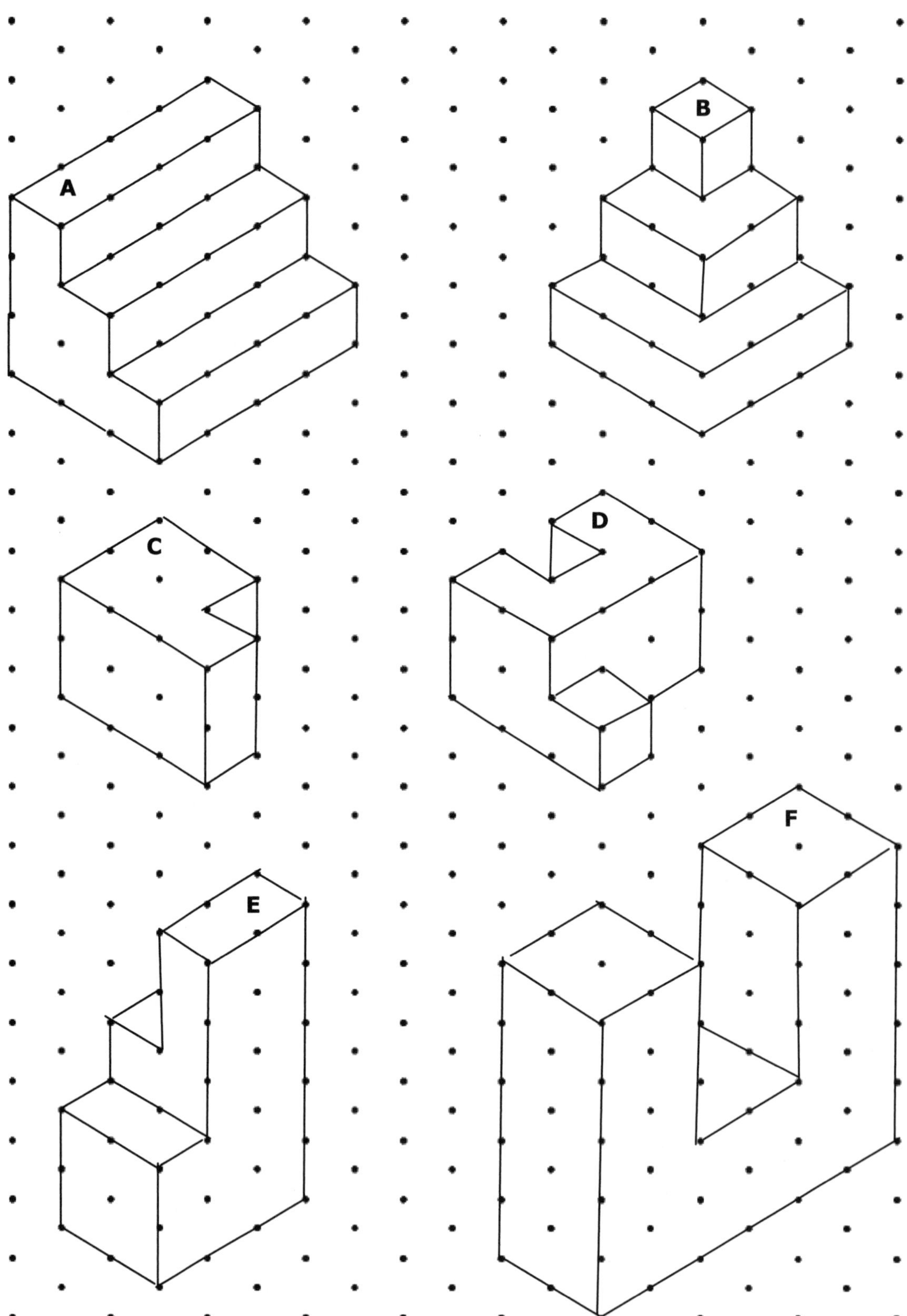
A
B
C
D
E
F

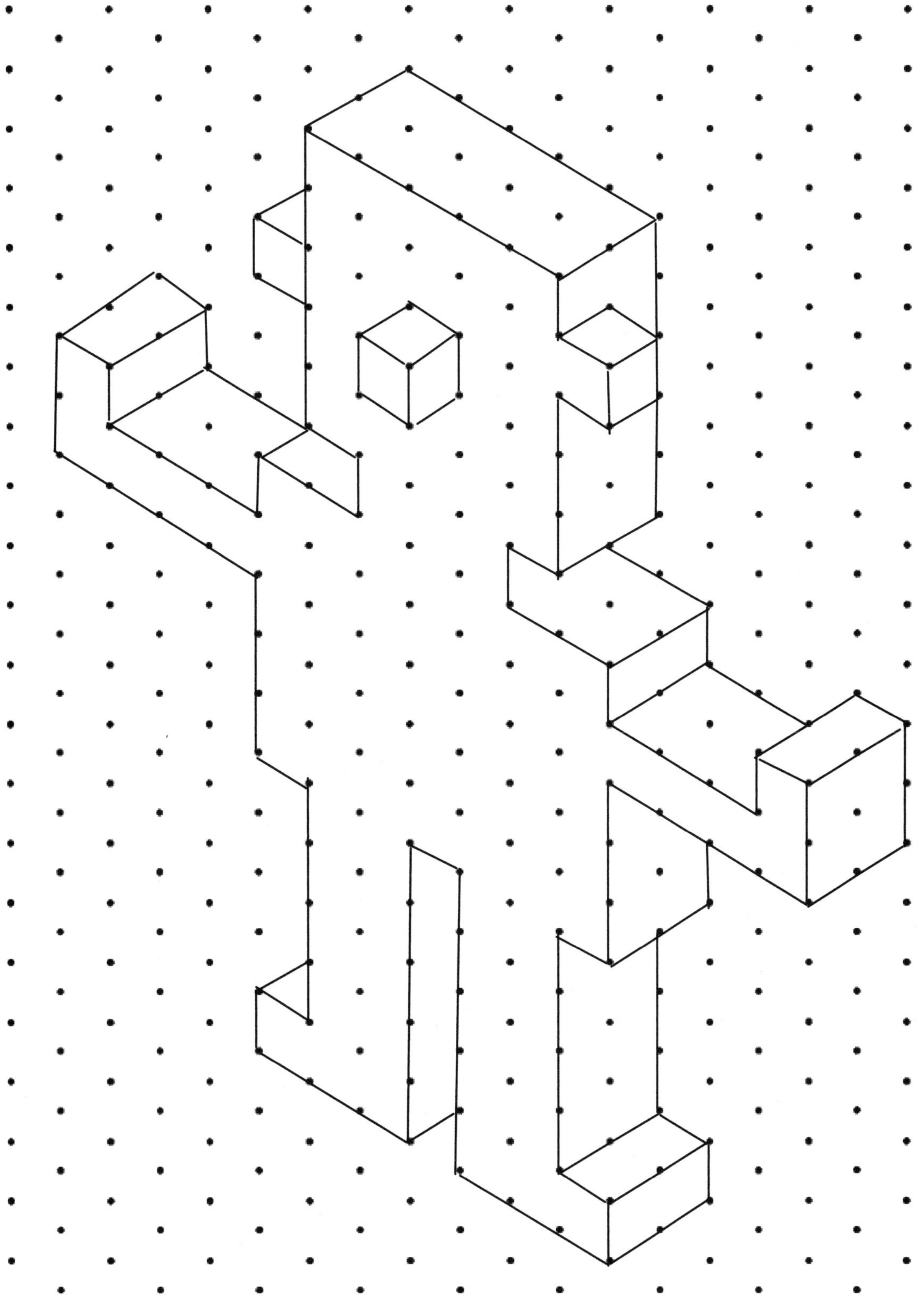

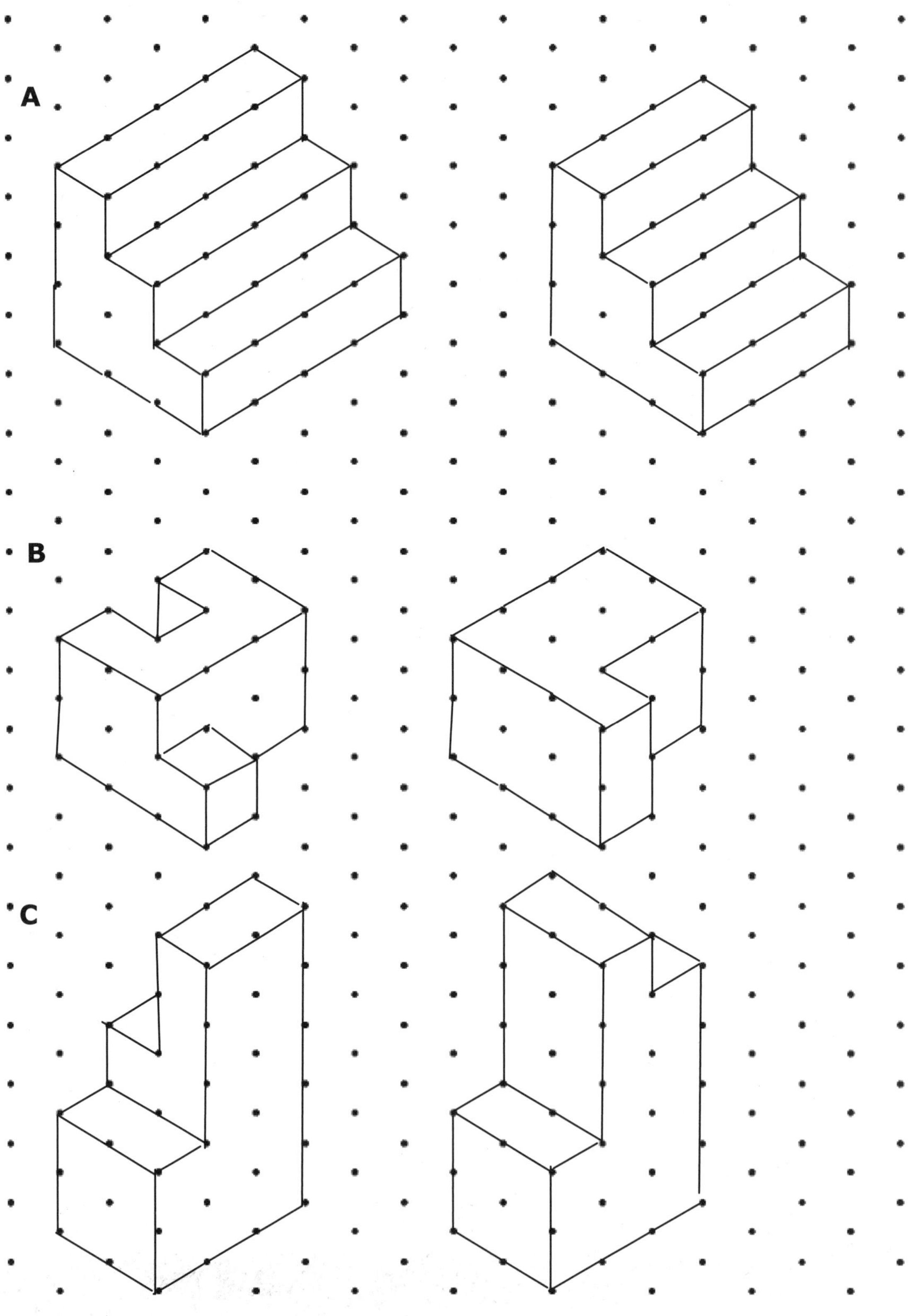
A
B
C